Contents

Summarizing Strategies Grade 2, SV 9781419099861

Introduction

Throughout their school career, students are asked to read a variety of materials, from long stories and challenging poems to brief, informative articles and in-depth reports. Regardless of the genre and length of what they read, students must be able to summarize new information. A *summary* is a brief statement that tells the important points of a work of fiction or the main ideas of a work of nonfiction.

Summarizing is a fundamental reading and study skill. Young readers who master this skill have a powerful tool that helps them
- check their comprehension of what they have read.
- create their own materials for later study and review.
- organize information in various patterns.
- paraphrase new information in words that are meaningful to them.
- perform better on standardized test items that require summary.

Not only does summarizing help students gauge their reading comprehension, it reveals the underlying organizational patterns of writing. Students can then use these patterns as they write their own fiction and nonfiction pieces.

In early grades, summarizing is often taught in conjunction with identifying main idea and important details. As students progress, they learn to extract important information from a greater variety of genres and to generalize, draw conclusions, and make inferences as part of summarizing.

This series, *Summarizing Strategies,* is comprised of five books (Grades 2–6) and suggests a variety of techniques to encourage summarizing skill development. Each book targets 21 different strategies and employs a diverse collection of graphic organizers to assist students in visualizing how summaries are formed. Graphic organizers are critical components that serve as scaffolding necessary for students to structure their summaries and make connections between the targeted strategy and summarizing.

The strategies are logically sequenced from most basic to most difficult. Students begin by looking for the main idea and supporting details. As they progress through the book, students will encounter increasingly complex skills that require them to use higher-order thinking skills.

Features

Each of the 21 strategies follows a four-page sequence. The first page contains a completed model graphic organizer and summary based on the targeted strategy.

Students first learn about the strategy they will practice.

Sample reading selection is geared toward targeted summarizing strategy.

A completed model is provided for students to follow.

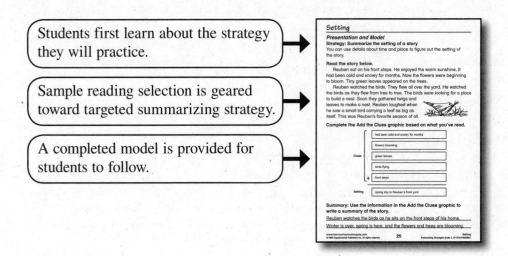

The second and third pages of each section provide reading passages adapted for each strategy. After reading each story, students continue to the worksheet page to complete the graphic organizer and write a summary based on what they have read in the story.

Students may practice reading independently, in small groups, or with the whole class.

Simple, clean designs and illustrations allow for clear photocopies and easy-to-read transparencies.

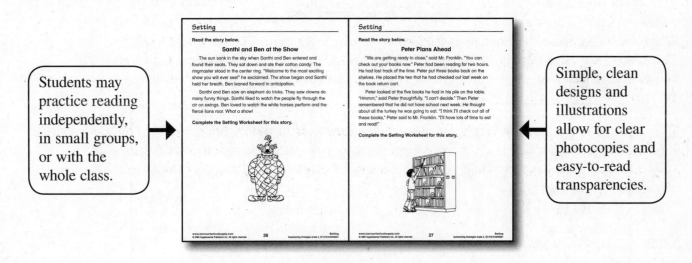

Summarizing Strategies Grade 2, SV 9781419099861

The fourth page in each section is a worksheet featuring a specific graphic organizer created for each strategy. These worksheets are designed for use with the provided texts as well as any other readings the teacher may choose, allowing for extra practice as needed. Worksheet pages are easily found by looking for the Teacher's Toolbox icon:

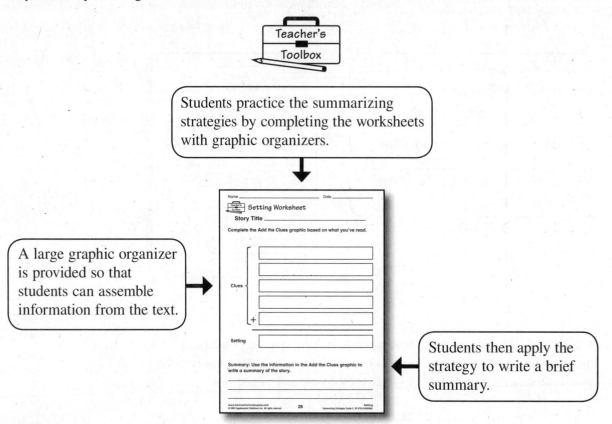

Students practice the summarizing strategies by completing the worksheets with graphic organizers.

A large graphic organizer is provided so that students can assemble information from the text.

Students then apply the strategy to write a brief summary.

When compiled, these 21 template pages form a Teacher's Toolbox of Graphic Organizers. This feature has been designed to allow flexibility and adaptation for a wide range of texts and student skill levels.

Teacher's Toolbox of Graphic Organizers

Web Diagram	8	Circular Cycle	52
Main Idea/Detail Table	12	Cause and Effect Flowchart	56
Wheel and Spokes	16	Context Clues Chart	60
Chain Links	20	Venn Diagram	64
Story Map	24	Character Profile Diagram	68
Add the Clues	28	Prediction Chart	72
Sequence Chart	32	Q Matrix	76
Problem and Solution Puzzle	36	Everything Points to It	80
Main Idea Diagram	40	Follow the Clues	84
Supporting Details Bridge	44	Author's Purpose Flowchart	88
Related Details Chart	48		

Summarizing Strategies uses a variety of techniques to improve students' abilities to summarize. With continued practice in summarizing, students should improve their reading comprehension skills and standardized test scores.

Main Idea

Presentation and Model

Strategy: Finding the important parts of a story to tell the main idea.
A story may tell about many things. The main idea tells what a story is
mostly about.

Read the story below.

Max has a little spotted dog named Wags. They
play together after school. Max also has two pet rabbits.
One of the rabbits is light brown and very large. The
other rabbit is small and white with pink eyes. Last week
Max bought three goldfish. He feeds them twice a day. Max's
family of pets keeps growing!

Complete the Web Diagram based on what you've read.

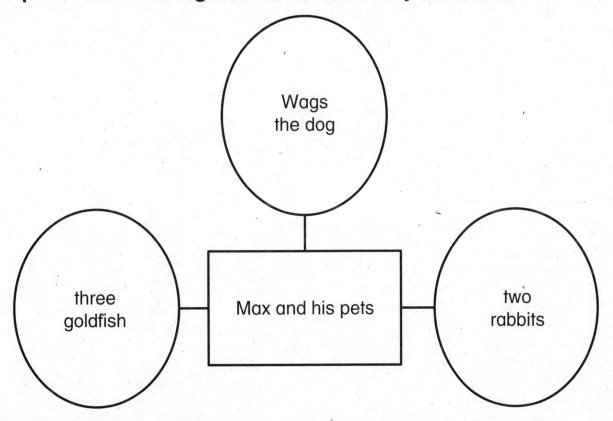

**Summary: Use the information in the Web Diagram to write
a summary of the story. Include the main idea.**

Max has lots of pets. Max has a dog, two rabbits, and three

goldfish.

Summarizing Strategies Grade 2, SV 9781419099861

Main Idea

Read the story below.

Mai Paints

Mai wanted to paint a picture for the school art show. First, she spread some newspaper on the floor to keep it clean. She did not want to make a mess. Next, she set up her easel and her paints. Mai found some large sheets of paper and paintbrushes. Then she filled an old plastic cup with water so she could wash her paintbrushes. Finally, Mai clipped one of the sheets of paper to the easel. Now she was ready to paint!

Complete the Main Idea Worksheet for this story.

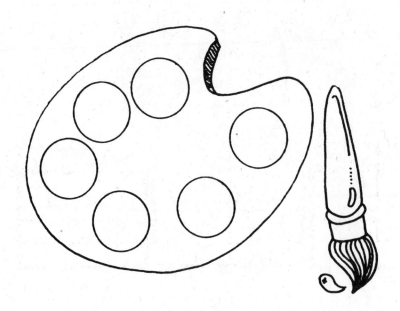

Summarizing Strategies Grade 2, SV 9781419099861

Main Idea

Read the story below.

Justin at the Zoo

Justin helped at the zoo. Sometimes he helped get the food ready for the animals. Other times he helped wash the dishes that the animals ate from. The dishes needed to be clean. Justin liked feeding the baby animals best. He was able to hold the animals and feed them with a bottle.

Complete the Main Idea Worksheet for this story.

Summarizing Strategies Grade 2, SV 9781419099861

Name _____ Date _____

 Teacher's Toolbox

Main Idea Worksheet

Story Title _____

Complete the Web Diagram based on what you've read.

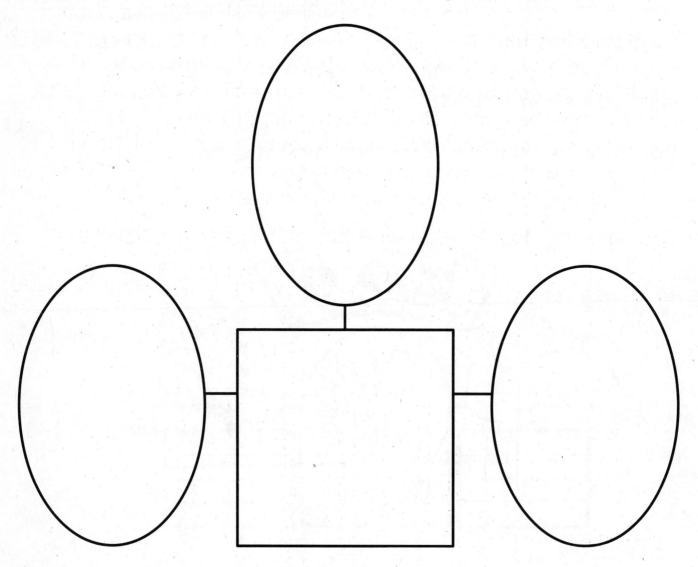

Summary: Use the information in the Web Diagram to write a summary of the story. Include the main idea.

_____

_____

_____

Main Idea
Summarizing Strategies Grade 2, SV 9781419099861

Supporting Details

Presentation and Model

Strategy: Finding details that support the main idea

Supporting details are parts of a story that give more information about the main idea. When summarizing, it is important to find details that support the main idea.

Read the story below.

    Ann loves to write all sorts of stories. Once, she made up a story about a talking fish. She wrote down her story and drew pictures, too. Another story she wrote was all about pirates. Last week Ann wrote a make-believe story about a boy who rode a bull to school. Now Ann is busy writing about a secret cabin in the woods! Who knows what she'll write next?

Complete the Main Idea/Detail Table based on what you've read.

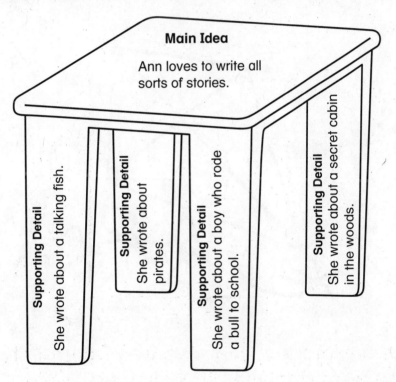

Main Idea

Ann loves to write all sorts of stories.

Supporting Detail She wrote about a talking fish.

Supporting Detail She wrote about pirates.

Supporting Detail She wrote about a boy who rode a bull to school.

Supporting Detail She wrote about a secret cabin in the woods.

Summary: Use the information in the Main Idea/Detail Table to write a summary of the story.

Ann loves to write all sorts of stories. She wrote about a talking fish, pirates, a boy and a bull, and a secret cabin.

Summarizing Strategies Grade 2, SV 9781419099861

Supporting Details

Read the story below.

Sandy Flies a Kite

Sandy got ready to fly her brand new kite. She went to a big, empty soccer field so she wouldn't be near lots of trees. She wanted to make sure her kite would not get caught in a tree. It was a perfect day. The sun was shining and the wind was blowing softly. It was just enough wind to gently lift the kite. Sandy slowly let out the string. She watched her kite go up in the air. It seemed to dance in the sky.

Complete the Supporting Details Worksheet for this story.

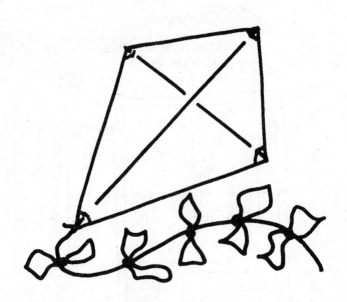

Summarizing Strategies Grade 2, SV 9781419099861

Supporting Details

Read the story below.

More Than a Game

Arturo loves everything about basketball. He likes to shoot baskets. Whoosh! He can throw the ball right through the net. Arturo can bounce the ball very fast, too. He can also throw the ball to his teammates very quickly. You have never seen someone jump as high as Arturo either. Someday, Arturo wants to play basketball in college. He hopes to become a basketball coach, too.

Complete the Supporting Details Worksheet for this story.

Summarizing Strategies Grade 2, SV 9781419099861

Name _____   Date _____

Supporting Details Worksheet

Story Title _____

Complete the Main Idea/Detail Table based on what you've read.

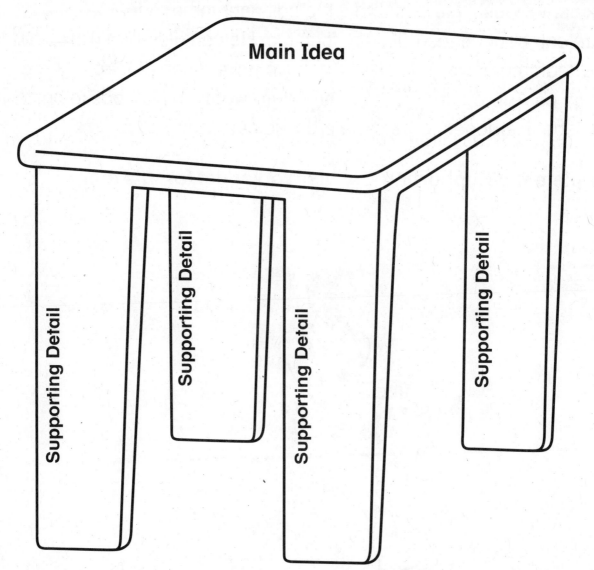

Main Idea

Supporting Detail

Supporting Detail

Supporting Detail

Supporting Detail

Summary: Use the information in the Main Idea/Detail Table to write a summary of the story.

_____

_____

_____

Creating a Summary

Presentation and Model
Strategy: Using important information to summarize a story

When you tell a short form of a story in your own words, you are making a summary. A summary tells the main idea and important details.

Read the story below.

Tyrone was sad because he could not go out and play. He watched his two brothers and their friends play outside. Tyrone had broken his arm the day before, and he was sad.

"Tyrone, why don't you read a book?" his father asked.

"No, I don't feel like it." Tyrone just sat and looked out the window. He played with his cat for a little while.

When the doorbell rang, Tyrone thought that one of his brother's friends had come by. But instead, it was his friend Seth. "Since you can't play outside, I brought some games over for us to play." Tyrone smiled broadly. Maybe the day was going to be fun after all.

Complete the Wheel and Spokes based on what you've read.

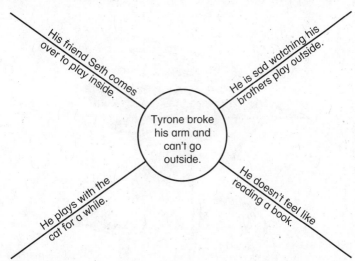

His friend Seth comes over to play inside.

He is sad watching his brothers play outside.

Tyrone broke his arm and can't go outside.

He plays with the cat for a while.

He doesn't feel like reading a book.

Summary: Use the information in the Wheel and Spokes to write a summary of the story.

Tyrone is sad because he broke his arm and can't play outside. He does not feel like reading, so he plays with his cat. The doorbell rings and he is happy because his friend Seth came over.

Summarizing Strategies Grade 2, SV 9781419099861

Creating a Summary

Read the story below.

Summer Fun

    The Hernandez family goes camping every summer. They camp for a whole month. Sometimes they camp at the beach. They like to look for shells. One time they camped in a state park. They pitched their tent in the woods. They had fun watching deer, birds, and frogs. Another time, the Hernandez family camped by a lake. They went swimming. They also caught lots of fish. Their favorite place to camp is in the mountains. They hike on trails and take lots of pictures of the view below. One time they even spotted an eagle soaring over the mountaintop. That was a sight they would never forget.

Complete the Creating a Summary Worksheet for this story.

Creating a Summary

Read the story below.

The Baby Ducks

Lamont's family lived near a pond. Lamont loved to go to the pond. One day Lamont sat on a log at the edge of the pond. He saw a mother duck. She was sitting on her eggs. Every day Lamont sat near the pond and watched the mother duck. One day the eggs hatched. The baby ducks waddled over to their mother.

Each day after school Lamont watched the ducks. Sometimes the baby ducks ran behind their mother. Other times they swam with her in the pond. One day Lamont was in for a surprise. Quack! Quack! Quack! The mother duck and the little ducks ran up to greet Lamont.

Complete the Creating a Summary Worksheet for this story.

Summarizing Strategies Grade 2, SV 9781419099861

Name _____ Date _____

Creating a Summary Worksheet

Story Title _____

Complete the Wheel and Spokes based on what you've read.

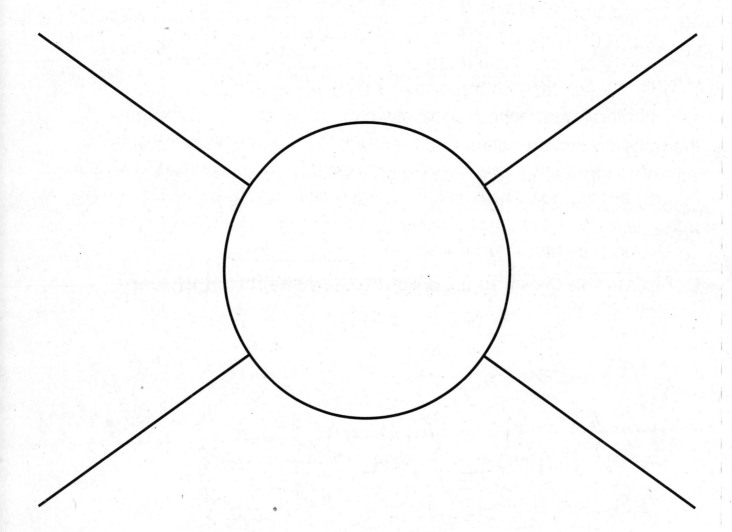

Summary: Use the information in the Wheel and Spokes to write a summary of the story.

_____

_____

_____

Connecting Story Parts

Presentation and Model
Strategy: Making connections between characters, events, and objects in a story

When we summarize, we need to understand how the people, events, and things in a story are related to one another.

Read the story below.

Leisha and her friend Tony went to the zoo. They saw all kinds of animals. The monkeys were swinging from limb to limb. A diver fed fish that were swimming in a big glass tank. They were having a great day.

Leisha's favorite animal was a small white polar bear. Tony loved watching the seals flip and swim through the water. The two friends were having such a good time that they didn't even know it was time for the zoo to close. They were surprised when they saw a clock that showed 5:00, and they had to go home.

Complete the Chain Links based on what you've read.

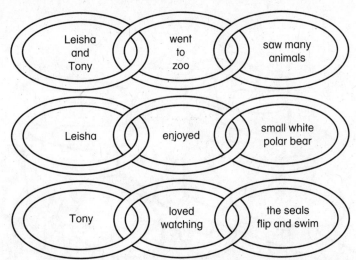

Summary: Use the information in the Chain Links to write a summary of the story.

Leisha and Tony went to the zoo and had a great day. They saw all sorts of animals. Leisha's favorite was a polar bear, while Tony loved the seals. They were surprised when it was time to go home.

Connecting Story Parts

Read the story below.

Michael's Birthday Boxes

Michael and his family got together in the living room at Michael's house. It was Michael's birthday. He was wishing and hoping for a pair of roller skates. He opened a small yellow present from his uncle first. In it was a slip of paper that read, "Open the red box for a big surprise."

"Hmmm," said Michael, puzzled. He opened the red box and found another slip of paper. It read, "Open the blue box for a big surprise." Michael smiled and looked at his uncle. He opened the blue box and could hardly believe it. Inside was a pair of skates just like he wanted.

Complete the Connecting Story Parts Worksheet for this story.

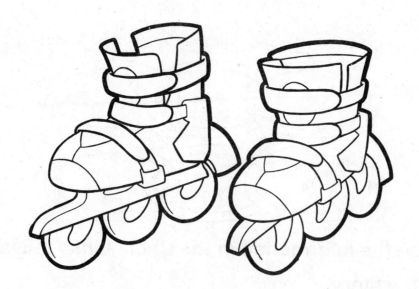

Connecting Story Parts

Read the story below.

Jacob Starts a Story

Today in class, Ms. Reyna told everyone to write a story. "First, I want you to jot down a list of the things that interest you." Jacob got out a sheet of blank paper. He made a list of all sorts of things. He listed pirates, horses, space shuttles, and George Washington.

Jacob raised his hand. "Ms. Reyna, what should I do?" he asked. "I'll never think of a story. I don't know a lot about any of the things on my list."

Mrs. Reyna said, "Usually, it's a good idea to write about things that you like." Jacob looked around the room and thought for a moment. He saw his best friend Hans scribbling away. Jacob thought about all the fun he and Hans had together. "Hans is my best friend," Jacob said to himself. "I think I know just what to write about!"

Complete the Connecting Story Parts Worksheet for this story.

Summarizing Strategies Grade 2, SV 9781419099861

Name _____   Date _____

Connecting Story Parts Worksheet

Story Title _____

Complete the Chain Links based on what you've read. Write a person or people in the first link, an event in the second link, and the other things about the event in the third link.

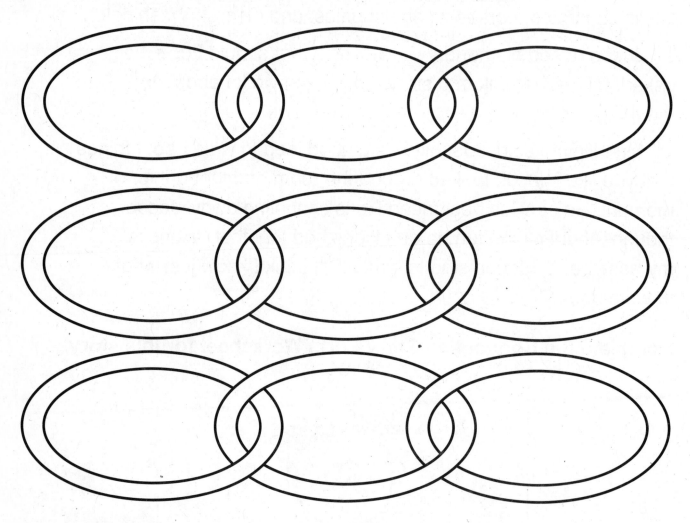

Summary: Use the information in the Chain Links to write a summary of the story.

_____

_____

_____

Summarizing Strategies Grade 2, SV 9781419099861

Story Elements

Presentation and Model

Strategy: Using story elements to summarize a story

A story map can be used to help summarize a story. A story map usually tells about the main character, the setting, and important events in the story.

Read the story below.

Mr. Flores is working in his garage. He has a workbench with lots of tools there. He has hammers, saws, and screwdrivers. He has lots of electric tools, too. Mr. Flores is making a rocking horse for his granddaughter. His friend Pete is helping him.

"I'll cut out the pieces for the rocking horse," said Pete. Next, Pete sanded the wood so it would be smooth.

Mr. Flores put all the pieces together. "Almost done," he said. Finally, Mr. Flores painted the rocking horse.

Complete the Story Map based on what you've read.

Characters
Mr. Flores; Pete

Setting
Mr. Flores's garage

Events
Pete cuts the wood.

Pete sands the wood.

Mr. Flores puts the pieces together.

Mr. Flores paints the rocking horse.

Summary: Use the information in the Story Map to write a summary of the story.

Mr. Flores builds a rocking horse in his garage. He and his friend Pete use many tools. Pete cuts the wood and sands it, while Mr. Flores puts the pieces together and paints the rocking horse.

Story Elements
Summarizing Strategies Grade 2, SV 9781419099861

Story Elements

Read the story below.

Claudia's Big Move

Claudia's family moved. They left Texas. They moved to New Hampshire. Claudia's father drove a big truck across the United States. All their things were inside. Her mother drove the car. Sometimes Claudia rode in the truck. Sometimes she rode in the car.

It took one week for Claudia's family to get to the new house. They moved all their things into the house. Claudia set up her bedroom. She unpacked all of her toys, clothes, and furniture. She put everything away neatly. She was happy to sleep in her own bed at night.

Complete the Story Elements Worksheet for this story.

Story Elements

Read the story below.

Amit's Aunt

Amit's family went to visit his aunt. They all rode on a train. They saw lots of snow and five lakes. They saw many forests. It was very beautiful. Amit's aunt was waiting for them when their train came in.

"Come here and let me give you all a hug!" Amit's aunt cried out. They all chatted excitedly on the ride from the train station. Amit's aunt lived on a ranch with many horses. Amit and his family had fun riding the horses. Soon it was time to go home. Everyone was sad to leave, but they knew they would visit again.

Complete the Story Elements Worksheet for this story.

Name _____ Date _____

Story Elements Worksheet

Story Title _____

Complete the Story Map based on what you've read.

> **Characters**

> **Setting**

> **Events**

Summary: Use the information in the Story Map to write a summary of the story.

_____

_____

_____

Story Elements
Summarizing Strategies Grade 2, SV 9781419099861

Setting

Presentation and Model
Strategy: Summarize the setting of a story

You can use details about time and place to figure out the setting of the story.

Read the story below.

Reuben sat on his front steps. He enjoyed the warm sunshine. It had been cold and snowy for months. Now the flowers were beginning to bloom. Tiny green leaves appeared on the trees.

Reuben watched the birds. They flew all over the yard. He watched the birds as they flew from tree to tree. The birds were looking for a place to build a nest. Soon they gathered twigs and leaves to make a nest. Reuben laughed when he saw a small bird carrying a leaf as big as itself. This was Reuben's favorite season of all.

Complete the Add the Clues graphic based on what you've read.

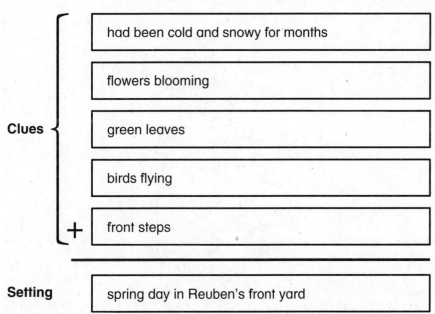

Clues

| had been cold and snowy for months |
| flowers blooming |
| green leaves |
| birds flying |
| front steps |

Setting: spring day in Reuben's front yard

Summary: Use the information in the Add the Clues graphic to write a summary of the story.

Reuben watches the birds as he sits on the front steps of his home.

Winter is over, spring is here, and the flowers and trees are blooming.

Summarizing Strategies Grade 2, SV 9781419099861

Setting

Read the story below.

Santhi and Ben at the Show

The sun sank in the sky when Santhi and Ben entered and found their seats. They sat down and ate their cotton candy. The ringmaster stood in the center ring. "Welcome to the most exciting show you will ever see!" he exclaimed. The show began and Santhi held her breath. Ben leaned forward in anticipation.

Santhi and Ben saw an elephant do tricks. They saw clowns do many funny things. Santhi liked to watch the people fly through the air on swings. Ben loved to watch the white horses perform and the fierce lions roar. What a show!

Complete the Setting Worksheet for this story.

Summarizing Strategies Grade 2, SV 9781419099861

Setting

Read the story below.

Peter Plans Ahead

"We are getting ready to close," said Mr. Franklin. "You can check out your books now." Peter had been reading for two hours. He had lost track of the time. Peter put three books back on the shelves. He placed the two that he had checked out last week on the book return cart.

Peter looked at the five books he had in his pile on the table. "Hmmm," said Peter thoughtfully. "I can't decide." Then Peter remembered that he did not have school next week. He thought about all the turkey he was going to eat. "I think I'll check out all of these books," Peter said to Mr. Franklin. "I'll have lots of time to eat and read!"

Complete the Setting Worksheet for this story.

Name _____ Date _____

Setting Worksheet

Story Title _____

Complete the Add the Clues graphic based on what you've read.

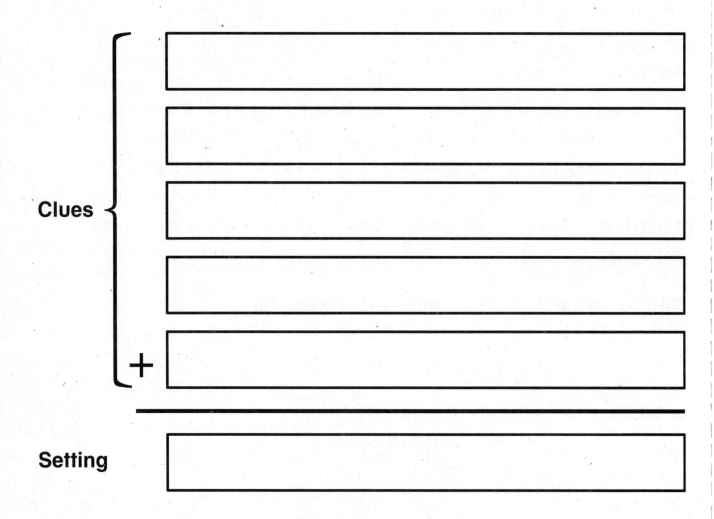

Clues {

\+

_____

Setting

Summary: Use the information in the Add the Clues graphic to write a summary of the story.

_____

_____

_____

Summarizing Strategies Grade 2, SV 9781419099861

Sequence of Events

Presentation and Model
Strategy: Summarize the sequence of events in a story

A sequence of events is the order that events happen in a story. Writing down these steps in order can help you remember them.

Read the story below.

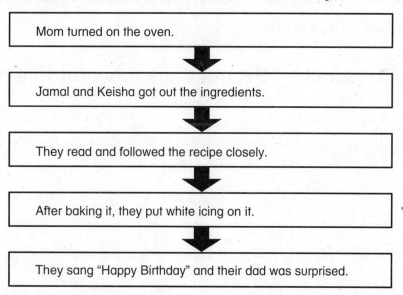

Jamal and Keisha wanted to do something special for their dad's birthday. They decided to make a cake.

They found a recipe. Their mom turned the oven on for them so it would get hot. Jamal and Keisha got out flour, sugar, and eggs. "Let's make sure to follow the recipe closely," said Jamal. "We want this cake to turn out perfectly." Keisha nodded in agreement. After their mom helped them bake the cake, they put white icing on it.

Jamal and Keisha were proud of their cake. When their dad got home, they sang "Happy Birthday." Dad was surprised.

Complete the Sequence Chart based on what you've read.

Mom turned on the oven.
↓
Jamal and Keisha got out the ingredients.
↓
They read and followed the recipe closely.
↓
After baking it, they put white icing on it.
↓
They sang "Happy Birthday" and their dad was surprised.

Summary: Use the information in the Sequence Chart to write a summary of the story.

Jamal and Keisha wanted to bake a cake for their dad's birthday.

Their mother turned on the oven and they got out the ingredients.

They followed the recipe closely, and their dad was surprised.

Summarizing Strategies Grade 2, SV 9781419099861

Sequence of Events

Read the story below.

Dad's Trick

Mia loved to do all sorts of tricks. One day Mia's dad showed her a special trick. First, he blew up a balloon and tied the end tightly. Then he placed a small piece of clear tape on the balloon. "I am going to stick a pin in this balloon," said Mia's dad. "What do you think will happen?"

Mia laughed. "It's going to pop!" Mia's dad carefully stuck the pin in the balloon. The balloon did not pop. "How did you do that?" Mia asked.

"It's easy!" said her dad. "I stuck the balloon in the spot where I put the tape." Mia's dad explained that the tape is stronger than the balloon. He told her that air will leak out but the balloon won't pop. Mia laughed at her dad's trick.

Complete the Sequence of Events Worksheet for this story.

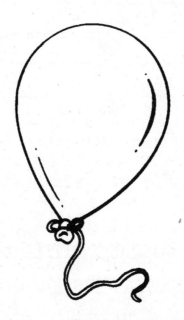

Summarizing Strategies Grade 2, SV 9781419099861

Sequence of Events

Read the story below.

The Three Squirrels

Three little squirrels got ready for winter. The first squirrel said, "I have lots of time to gather nuts. Today I'm going to run and play in the woods." So off she went.

The second squirrel watched. He thought to himself, "Hmmm, I'd like to play in the fall leaves too." So the second squirrel quickly gathered a few nuts and went off to play.

The third squirrel watched the other two squirrels play. "I'll have plenty of time to play later on," she said. "But right now I need to gather nuts for winter." When winter finally came, the first two squirrels sat hungry inside a hollow tree. The third squirrel laughed and played in the snow. She had plenty of food and lots of time for fun!

Complete the Sequence of Events Worksheet for this story.

Summarizing Strategies Grade 2, SV 9781419099861

Name _____ Date _____

Sequence of Events Worksheet

Story Title _____

Complete the Sequence Chart based on what you've read.

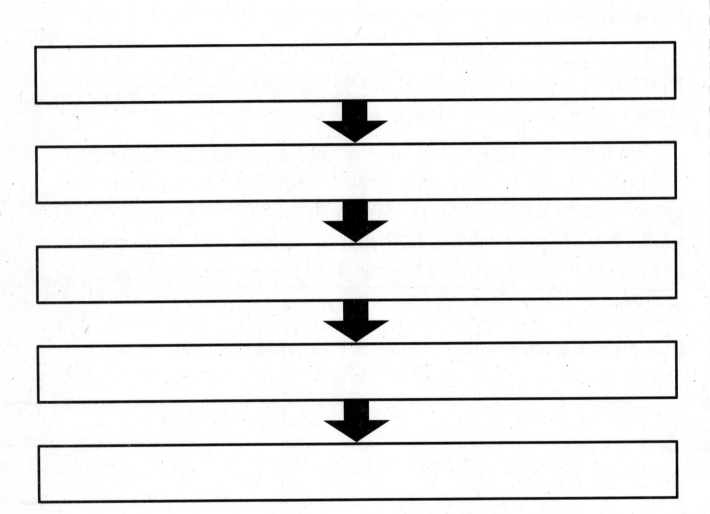

Summary: Use the information in the Sequence Chart to write a summary of the story.

_____

_____

Problems and Solutions

Presentation and Model

Strategy: Identify the problem and solution in a story

Characters in a story often face a problem. The answer to the problem is called the solution.

Read the story below.

Sam got a new puppy named Rex. Rex liked to jump and play with Sam. But when Sam told Rex to do things, Rex would not listen. Once Sam said, "Roll over, Rex." But Rex did not roll over. Rex jumped up and licked Sam in the face. Another time Sam said, "Sit, Rex! Sit!" Rex did not listen. He rolled over and wagged his tail.

"What am I going to do with you, Rex?" said Sam. One day Sam took Rex for a walk. They passed a puppy school. "I think this is the right place for us, Rex." Rex jumped up and licked Sam's face. Sam smiled and laughed.

Complete the Problem and Solution Puzzle based on what you have read.

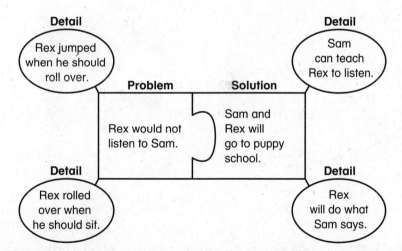

Detail
Rex jumped when he should roll over.

Detail
Sam can teach Rex to listen.

Problem
Rex would not listen to Sam.

Solution
Sam and Rex will go to puppy school.

Detail
Rex rolled over when he should sit.

Detail
Rex will do what Sam says.

Summary: Use the information in the Problem and Solution Puzzle to write a summary of the story.

Sam had a problem with his new puppy Rex. Rex would not do what

Sam told him to do. Sam decided to take Rex to a puppy school so he

could train Rex to listen.

Problems and Solutions

Read the story below.

The Old Lot

No one took care of the empty lot across the street from Lee's house. The grass had not been cut in a long time. It was full of tall weeds. There was a lot of trash, too. Loose papers and empty cans covered the lot. Lee was sad that no one played there.

One day Lee had an idea. Lee picked up the papers and empty cans. Lee placed the papers in a recycle bin. He brought the cans to a place where a city worker counted them. She gave Lee ten dollars for the cans. Lee used the money to buy flower seeds. Then Lee helped his dad cut the high grass. Now lots of children play in the empty lot!

Complete the Problems and Solutions Worksheet for this story.

Summarizing Strategies Grade 2, SV 9781419099861

Problems and Solutions

Read the story below.

Queen Hilda's Birthday

It was Queen Hilda's birthday. Everyone in the village loved their queen. On her birthday, all of the villagers gave Queen Hilda gifts. Many villagers saved money all year long to buy special things for the queen.

A hard-working gardener named Bert lived in the village. He loved the queen too. Bert wanted to give Queen Hilda a gift, too, but he had no money. Bert wondered what he could do.

Bert grew vegetables and flowers. He sold them at the market. This year there was very little rain. Bert was not able to grow many vegetables and flowers. Then he had an idea. He knew the queen loved flowers. He gave her some flower seeds. Queen Hilda loved them! She could plant them and have beautiful flowers.

Complete the Problems and Solutions Worksheet for this story.

Name _____ Date _____

Problems and Solutions Worksheet

Story Title _____

Complete the Problem and Solution Puzzle based on what you've read.

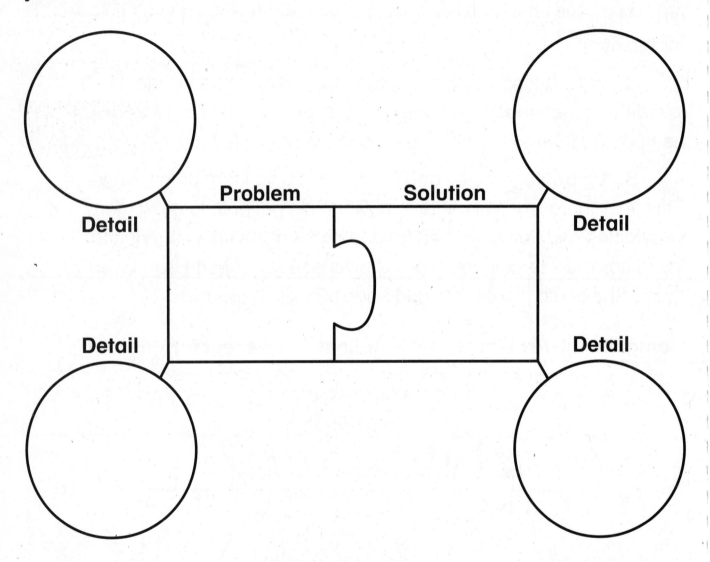

Summary: Use the information in the Problem and Solution Puzzle to write a summary of the story.

_____

_____

_____

          Summarizing Strategies Grade 2, SV 9781419099861

Main Idea for Nonfiction

Presentation and Model

Strategy: Finding the important parts of a text to tell the main idea

Sometimes a story gives facts and details. The main idea tells what a text is mostly about.

Read the text below.

Look in the sky. What do you see? In the daytime you can see the sun. The sun is a star. Look down at your feet. You can see a very important planet. You are standing on it right now. It is the planet Earth. Earth is one of eight planets that circle the sun.

What else can you see? Look in the sky at night. At night you can see the moon. You can also see many stars that twinkle in the night sky. There are millions of stars in the sky. You can't see most of them, but they are there!

Complete the Main Idea Diagram based on what you've read.

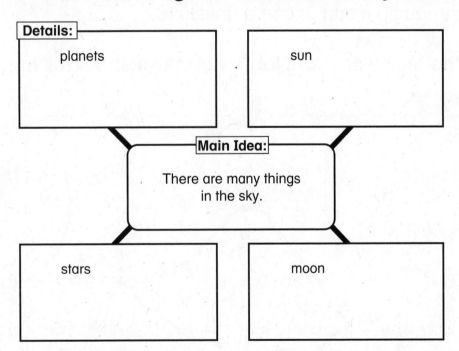

Details:
- planets
- sun

Main Idea:
There are many things in the sky.

- stars
- moon

Summary: Use the information in the Main Idea Diagram to write a summary of the text. Include the main idea.

The sun, the moon, planets, and stars are some of the many things in the sky.

Main Idea for Nonfiction

Read the text below.

Volcanoes

What causes a volcano? Deep in the ground it is very, very hot. It is so hot that rocks will melt. The melted rock becomes magma. Magma is thick and hot. Most of the time the magma stays deep in the earth.

More magma forms. There is not enough room underground for all of it. Pressure forms in the earth. Cracks appear along the surface of the earth. Sometimes these cracks are on land, and sometimes they are at the bottom of the ocean. Magma is forced through these cracks. As it cools down, it forms a thick mound. Over time the mound forms a volcano. If a volcano in the ocean grows large enough, it can become an island.

Complete the Main Idea for Nonfiction Worksheet for this text.

Main Idea for Nonfiction

Read the text below.

Bats

Bats are mammals. Their bodies are covered with fur. They have wings, but they are not birds. Birds hatch from eggs. Bats and other mammals do not hatch from eggs.

Bats eat insects. During the day, they hang upside down in dark places. They often live in caves or in dark spaces under bridges. Bats fly at night to find food. One bat can eat up to 1,000 insects an hour. Some bats live in places that get cold in the winter. These bats fly away in the fall. They fly to places that are warm in the winter. In the spring, they return again.

Complete the Main Idea for Nonfiction Worksheet for this text.

Name _____ Date _____

Main Idea for Nonfiction Worksheet

Text Title _____

Complete the Main Idea Diagram based on what you've read.

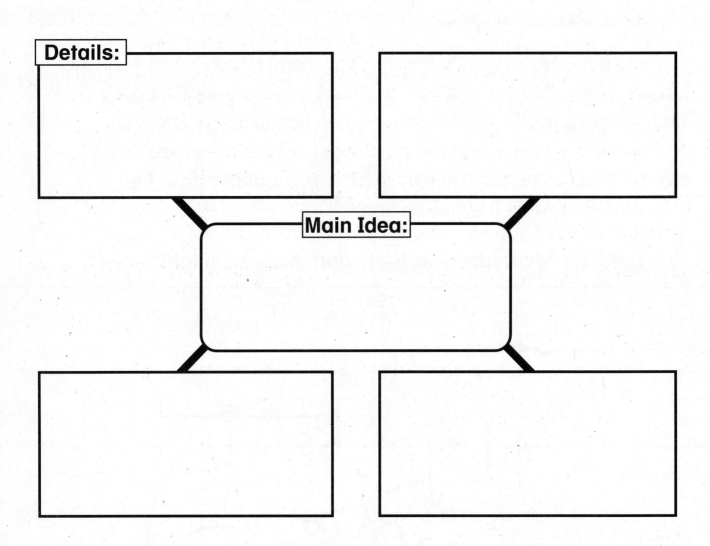

Summary: Use the information in the Main Idea Diagram to write a summary of the text. Include the main idea.

_____

_____

_____

Summarizing Strategies Grade 2, SV 9781419099861

Supporting Details for Nonfiction

Presentation and Model
Strategy: Finding details that support the main idea
Supporting details give more information about the main idea. When summarizing, it is important to tell a supporting detail from the main idea.

Read the text below.

Have you ever seen a prairie dog? They are not dogs. Prairie dogs belong to the squirrel family. Prairie dogs live together in towns they dig underground. Prairie dogs dig holes called burrows. They also dig tunnels to connect the burrows. This makes it easy for prairie dogs to move from place to place. Prairie dog towns can stretch for miles.

Prairie dogs dig lots of rooms. Some are for baby prairie dogs. Other rooms are for sleeping and storing food. Prairie dogs spend at least half of their life underground. Their prairie towns keep them warm in the winter and cool in the summer.

Complete the Supporting Details Bridge based on what you've read.

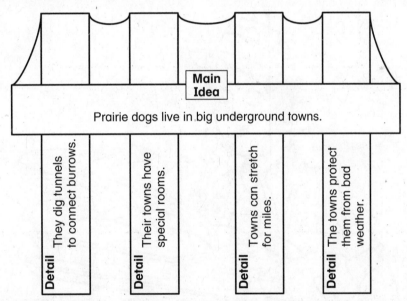

Main Idea

Prairie dogs live in big underground towns.

Detail: They dig tunnels to connect burrows.

Detail: Their towns have special rooms.

Detail: Towns can stretch for miles.

Detail: The towns protect them from bad weather.

Summary: Use the information in the Supporting Details Bridge to write a summary of the text.

Prairie dogs dig big underground towns made of burrows and tunnels.

Their towns have special rooms for resting and sleeping, and can

stretch for miles. Their towns protect them from bad weather.

Summarizing Strategies Grade 2, SV 9781419099861

Supporting Details for Nonfiction

Read the text below.

At the Bakery

A baker is a person who bakes in a bakery. A baker often makes bread. Bakers use yeast, water, salt, and flour to make bread. They can add other things too, like raisins, nuts, or honey.

A baker adds yeast to the water. The yeast bubbles in the water. The baker adds the flour and salt to make the dough. Bakers push and pull the dough and then set it aside. The dough rises in the bowl. Then the baker puts the dough in a pan and bakes it in the oven. Soon the bakery will have fresh bread to sell.

Complete the Supporting Details for Nonfiction Worksheet for this text.

Supporting Details for Nonfiction

Read the text below.

Skyscrapers

The world's tallest buildings are called skyscrapers. They seem to scrape the sky. Skyscrapers can be more than 100 floors high. You may wonder how skyscrapers are built.

The bottom of a skyscraper is buried below the earth. It is made from tons of concrete and steel. Once the bottom is in place, the tall part of the skyscraper is built. The frame of a skyscraper is made of steel. Think of a picture frame. It surrounds a picture and holds it in place. The steel frame of a skyscraper does the same thing. It holds the skyscraper in place. The next time you visit a big city, look up. You just may see a skyscraper or two!

Complete the Supporting Details for Nonfiction Worksheet for this text.

Supporting Details for Nonfiction Worksheet

Text Title _____

Complete the Supporting Details Bridge based on what you've read.

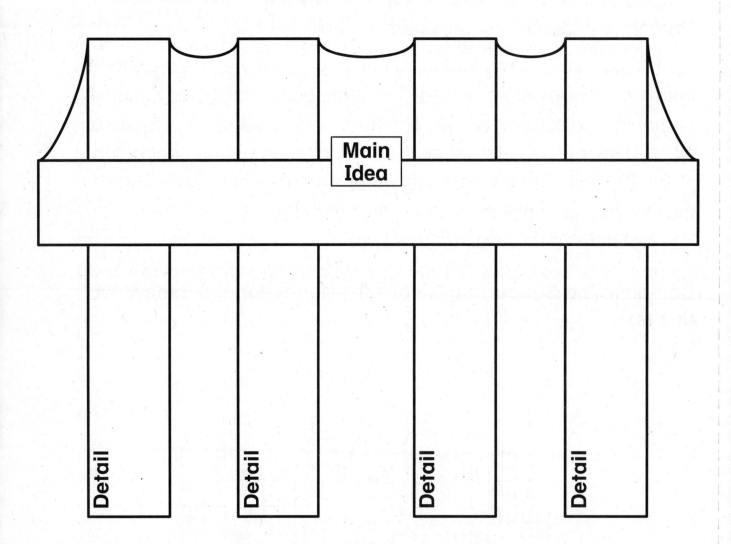

Summary: Use the information in the Supporting Details Bridge to write a summary of the text.

_____

_____

_____

Summaries for Nonfiction

Presentation and Model

Strategy: Using important information to summarize a text

A summary tells the main idea and important details. Sometimes these details can be closely related. Understanding how they are related can help you write a summary.

Read the text below.

There are many kinds of ants that live in an ant colony. Each ant has a special job. An ant colony always needs a queen ant. The queen ant lays the eggs. Without a queen there would be no colony. Some ants are worker ants. They do many different kinds of jobs in the colony. Some carry the queen's eggs to a special place inside the nest. Others make the nest bigger by digging new tunnels. Some worker ants carry the dirt from the tunnels outside of the nest. All ants in a colony work together. We can learn a lot from watching ants!

Complete the Related Details Chart based on what you've read.

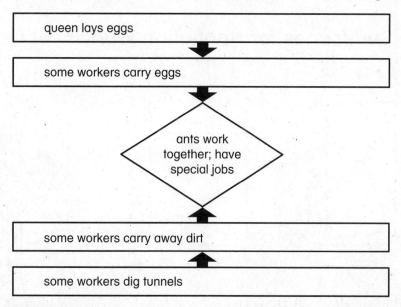

Summary: Use the information in the Related Details Chart to write a summary of the text.

Ants work together and have special jobs in an ant colony. The queen ant lays eggs and worker ants do many different jobs. They all work together.

Summarizing Strategies Grade 2, SV 9781419099861

Summaries for Nonfiction

Read the text below.

Life of a Cactus

A tiny cactus seed grows in the desert when it rains. A small cactus grows. It takes a long, long time. The cactus grows bigger. Then flowers start to appear. They are usually white or yellow, but they can also be orange or red. Birds, bees, and bats that live in the desert see the bright flowers. They fly over to the cactus. They sit on the cactus and drink the nectar from the flowers.

After a while, the flowers fall off. Small red fruit grows in their place. Desert animals eat the fruit. When the cactus grows bigger, it starts to grow "arms." After years and years go by, the cactus becomes very big and heavy. The tall cactus falls over. Now the cactus is home to desert animals that scurry along the ground.

Complete the Summaries for Nonfiction Worksheet for this text.

Summarizing Strategies Grade 2, SV 9781419099861

Summaries for Nonfiction

Read the text below.

The Rainforest

The rainforest is home to more different kinds of plants and animals than any place else on Earth. You might see insects like colorful butterflies or leaf cutter ants. Maybe you will see animals like monkeys or rare birds.

The rainforest is very steamy and damp. The leaves of the trees catch the rain. The rain runs down to the ground. It sinks into the soil. The roots soak up the water so the tree can grow. The rest of the water runs off into rivers and streams.

When you walk through the rainforest you can barely see the sky. That's because the leaves block out the sunlight. Above the treetops it is very sunny and bright.

Complete the Summaries for Nonfiction Worksheet for this text.

Summarizing Strategies Grade 2, SV 9781419099861

Name _____ Date _____

Summaries for Nonfiction Worksheet

Text Title _____

Complete the Related Details Chart based on what you've read.

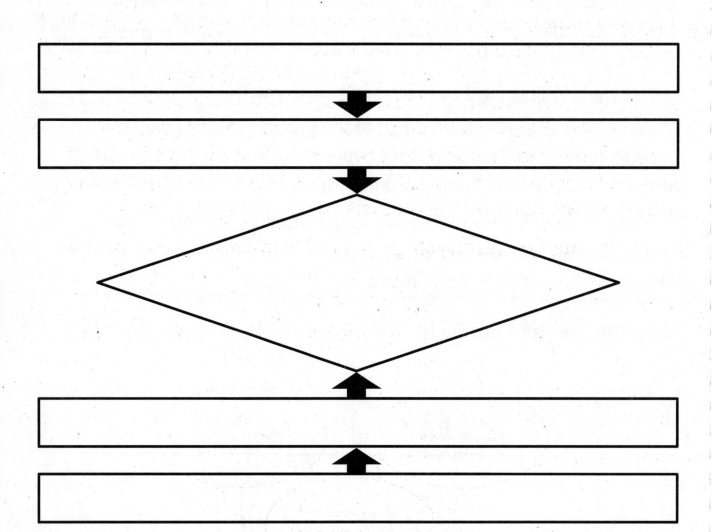

Summary: Use the information in the Related Details Chart to write a summary of the text.

_____

_____

_____

Summaries for Nonfiction
Summarizing Strategies Grade 2, SV 9781419099861

Parts of a Life Cycle

Presentation and Model
Strategy: Summarizing the parts of life cycle

The stages a living thing goes through from birth to adulthood is called a life cycle.

Read the text below.

A caterpillar goes through many changes in its life. At the end it becomes a butterfly. The two look very different.

A female butterfly lays eggs on a leaf. The eggs hatch, and tiny caterpillars come out to begin their lives. They eat to grow larger.

Next, the caterpillar forms a cocoon around itself. Many changes take place inside of the cocoon. About two weeks pass by. Now the adult butterfly is ready to come out. The cocoon splits open and the adult pushes its way out. Now the life cycle can begin again!

Complete the Circular Cycle graphic based on what you've read.

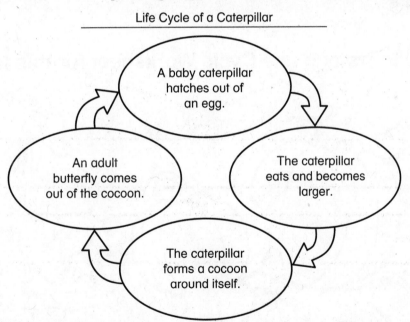

Life Cycle of a Caterpillar

A baby caterpillar hatches out of an egg.

The caterpillar eats and becomes larger.

The caterpillar forms a cocoon around itself.

An adult butterfly comes out of the cocoon.

Summary: Use the information in the Circular Cycle graphic to write a summary of the text.

A baby caterpillar hatches out of an egg and eats lots of leaves to

grow larger in size. Then the caterpillar forms a cocoon around itself.

After some time, an adult butterfly comes out of the cocoon.

Summarizing Strategies Grade 2, SV 9781419099861

Parts of a Life Cycle

Read the text below.

Pumpkins

Have you ever wondered how long it takes a pumpkin to grow?
A pumpkin starts from a small seed. You have probably seen the
seeds if you've ever cut into a pumpkin. The seeds are usually
planted in late spring. Most often they are planted in May or June.
After about ten days the seedlings push up through the soil.

Every day the plants grow a little bigger. Soon flowers appear on
the plants. Then they start to bloom. When they fall off, a pumpkin
takes its place. By July or August pumpkin vines cover the ground.
The pumpkin grows bigger and bigger. In no time at all October
arrives. Now it is time to pick the pumpkins. Guess what is inside?
Pumpkin seeds!

Complete the Parts of a Life Cycle Worksheet for this text.

Parts of a Life Cycle

Read the text below.

Forests Return

Animals flee as a fire spreads through a forest. Many plants and trees are burnt, but the forest is not gone forever. When the fire is over, some animals return. Insects feed on the trunks and roots of trees. Small animals look for seeds. Larger animals return too.

Soon new plants poke through the black earth. Grass and flowers begin to grow. Some trees grow new branches and leaves. Tiny tree seedlings grow from leftover seeds. More animals return. Young trees grow taller and taller. The forest is growing again!

Complete the Parts of a Life Cycle Worksheet for this text.

Summarizing Strategies Grade 2, SV 9781419099861

Name _____ Date _____

Parts of a Life Cycle Worksheet

Text Title _____

Complete the Circular Cycle graphic based on what you've read.

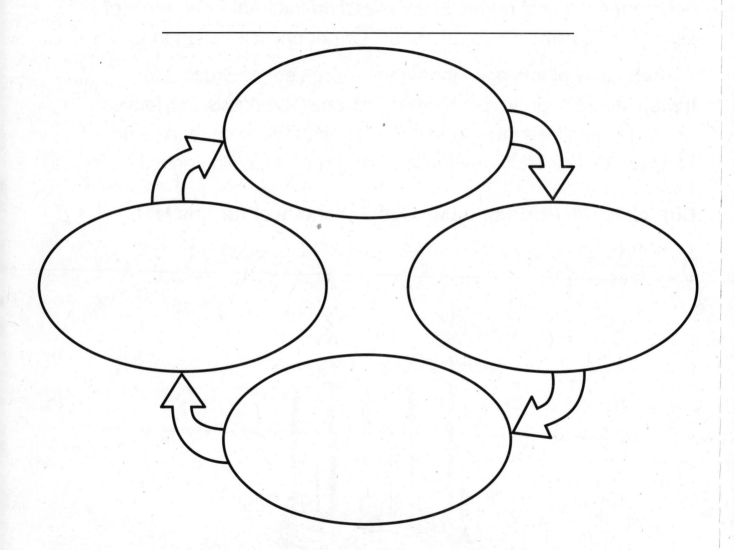

Summary: Use the information in the Circular Cycle graphic to write a summary of the text.

_____

_____

_____

Summarizing Strategies Grade 2, SV 9781419099861

Cause and Effect

Presentation and Model
Strategy: Identifying cause and effect in a story

A cause is what someone or something does to make something else happen. The effect is what happens because of a cause.

Read the story below.

Chris went outside to play in the frosty winter snow. He scooped up handfuls of snow and put the snow in a washtub. In no time at all Chris had built a snowman in the washtub.

Chris found two twigs to use for arms and got a carrot from inside for the nose. After he had finished, the sun peeked out from behind the clouds. After a while, Chris decided to go inside. The snowman began to melt. Plop! The snowman's nose fell off. Plop! Plop! The twig arms fell from its sides. When Chris came outside later, he had to laugh. All that was left of his snowman was a puddle in the washtub!

Complete the Cause and Effect Flowchart based on what you've read.

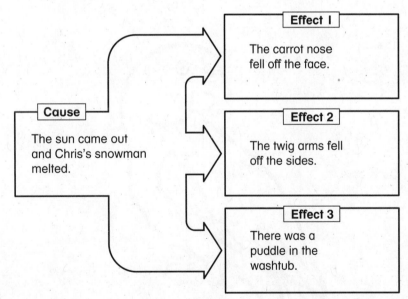

Cause

The sun came out and Chris's snowman melted.

Effect 1

The carrot nose fell off the face.

Effect 2

The twig arms fell off the sides.

Effect 3

There was a puddle in the washtub.

Summary: Use the information in the Cause and Effect Flowchart to write a summary of the story.

Chris built a snowman in a washtub. It began to melt. The carrot nose and the twig arms fell. All that was left was a puddle.

Cause and Effect
Summarizing Strategies Grade 2, SV 9781419099861

Cause and Effect

Read the story below.

Darius and Bud

Darius and his family have a parrot named Bud. Each day Darius and his sister take care of Bud. They take turns giving Bud clean, fresh water. They also fill Bud's food dish with a special seed mix. Once a week, they clean out the bottom of Bud's cage.

Darius loves to teach Bud how to talk. First, Darius repeats a short sentence many, many times. This way, Bud can hear the same words over and over. This helps Bud learn and remember what to say. Finally, Bud is able to repeat the sentence. Everyone laughs when Bud says, "This pretty bird can talk!"

Complete the Cause and Effect Worksheet for this story.

Cause and Effect
Summarizing Strategies Grade 2, SV 9781419099861

Cause and Effect

Read the story below.

Washing the Car

Dad got out the soap and hose. Jess turned on the water and filled a bucket, while Dad added the soap. Jess used the hose to get the car wet. Then Jess and Dad each grabbed a sponge. They washed the car from top to bottom.

Dad washed the roof and the front of the car. Jess washed the sides and the back of the car. The tires were very dirty, so Dad and Jess decided to wash the tires a second time. They rinsed all the soap off the car. Once the car was dry, it was shiny and clean. Mr. Jacobs from next door said, "What a beauty!" The judges at the car show said, "This sparkling car is the winner!"

Complete the Cause and Effect Worksheet for this story.

Name _____ Date _____

Cause and Effect Worksheet

Story Title _____

Complete the Cause and Effect Flowchart based on what you've read.

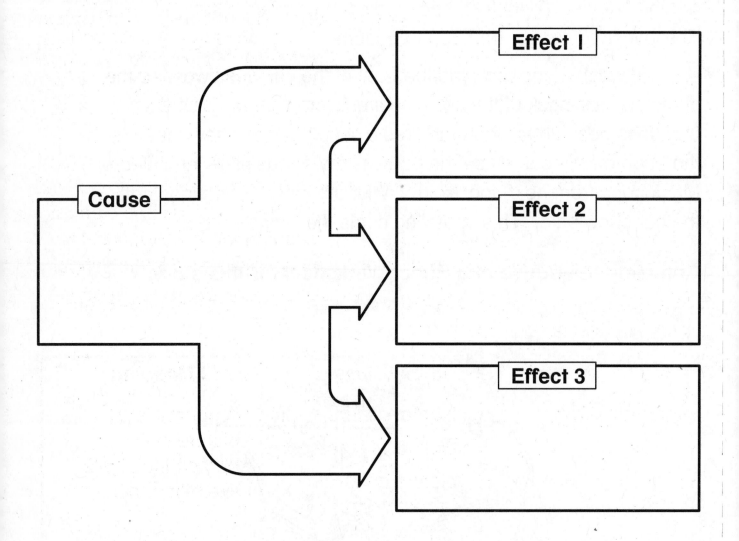

Summary: Use the information in the Cause and Effect Flowchart to write a summary of the story.

_____

_____

_____

Defining Words from Context

Presentation and Model

Strategy: Using an unfamiliar word and its meaning to write a summary

You can use words and sentences around an unfamiliar word to help you figure out the meaning of the word. These words and sentences are called context clues.

Read the story below.

When Maria was sick, she had to stay in bed. She read lots of magazines. She also read books. She played checkers and other games with her mother. She wrote a poem for her grandmother. Then she wrote a story for her father.

She also drew many pictures with her new crayons. Maria drew all kinds of pictures. After a while, Maria drew a special type of picture. It was a **portrait.** This one was special, though. It was not just a picture of any person. This one was a picture of her grandfather. It looked just like him! Before long, Maria was well. Maria was happy to go back to school.

Complete the Context Clues Chart for the word in <u>bold</u> based on what you've read.

Word	Context Clues	Word Meaning
portrait	type of picture; picture of a person; picture of her grandfather that looked just like him	A portrait is a picture of a person that looks like him or her.

Summary: Use the information in the Context Clues Chart to write a summary of the story.

Maria played games, read, and drew pictures while she was sick in bed. She drew a picture of her grandfather. Maria was glad to go back to her school.

Defining Words from Context

Read the story below.

Feeding Whiskers

Carly's little sister Jill wanted to help feed their cat Whiskers. Carly helped Jill hold the big bag of cat food. Jill used a big scoop to get the cat food out of the bag and put it into Whiskers' bowl.

Carly put Whiskers' milk bowl on the table and carefully poured the milk into it. Jill turned around. She did not see the bowl of milk. Jill's elbow **rammed** into the bowl. Smack! The bowl tipped over. The milk ran onto the floor. Just then, Whiskers ran over to the table. She lapped up the puddles of milk with her little pink tongue!

Complete the Defining Words from Context Worksheet for this story and the word in <u>bold</u>.

Summarizing Strategies Grade 2, SV 9781419099861

Defining Words from Context

Read the story below.

Lizards

Lizards never stop growing. But their skin does not grow with them. The skin becomes too small for the lizard's body. Like snakes, lizards **shed** their old skin. Often the lizard rubs its body on a rock or a branch. The old skin begins to peel off. Underneath is fresh, new skin.

Sometimes this skill can come in handy. For example, lizards called geckos have a neat trick. Their skin is very loose and comes off very easily when it is old. When another animal attacks a gecko, it can run free and the attacker is left holding the old skin!

Complete the Defining Words from Context Worksheet for this story and the word in <u>bold</u>.

Summarizing Strategies Grade 2, SV 9781419099861

Name _____   Date _____

Defining Words from Context Worksheet

Story Title _____

Complete the Context Clues Chart based on what you've read.

Word	Context Clues	Word Meaning

Summary: Use the information in the Context Clues Chart to write a summary of the story.

_____

_____

_____

Compare and Contrast

Presentation and Model

Strategy: Writing a summary using compare and contrast

When you compare, you look at how things are alike. When you contrast, you look at how things are different.

Read the story below.

Sarah and Casey are friends, but they are not alike. Sarah is tall with red hair and freckles. Casey is short with brown curly hair. Sarah likes to climb trees. She likes to run and jump. Casey likes to read. He also likes to draw and paint.

Sarah and Casey are both in second grade. They are both in Mr. Sudduth's class. On Thursday Sarah and Casey stay after school. They both go to chess club. On the weekends they often play chess together.

Complete the Venn Diagram based on what you've read.

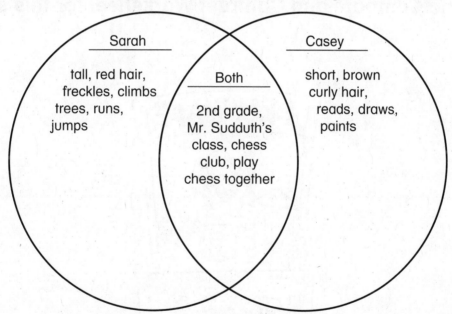

Sarah
tall, red hair, freckles, climbs trees, runs, jumps

Both
2nd grade, Mr. Sudduth's class, chess club, play chess together

Casey
short, brown curly hair, reads, draws, paints

Summary: Use the information in the Venn Diagram to write a summary of the story.

Casey and Sarah are both in second grade and enjoy chess and playing together. Casey and Sarah look different. Casey likes quiet activities, while Sarah enjoys outdoor activities.

Compare and Contrast

Read the story below.

The Lemonade Stand

Suki and Braxton wanted to earn money. They decided to set up a lemonade stand. Suki and Braxton squeezed the lemons and added water. Then Suki added sugar, while Braxton stirred. They set up their stand at the park.

Lots of people bought cups of lemonade. At the end of the day, Suki and Braxton counted the money. They made twenty dollars. Suki spent her half on a new puzzle. It was a rainforest puzzle. Braxton didn't want to spend his until later. He put his half in the bank.

Complete the Compare and Contrast Worksheet for this story.

Summarizing Strategies Grade 2, SV 9781419099861

Compare and Contrast

Read the story below.

Frogs and Toads

Frogs and toads have many things in common. Both hatch from eggs. As babies, frogs and toads live and grow in water. They are called tadpoles. Both are active at night. They sleep and rest in the daytime. Frogs and toads have long, sticky tongues. They do not have tails.

Frogs and toads are very different too. Frogs have smooth skin. Their skin feels damp when you touch it. Toads have dry, bumpy skin. Frogs live in or near water. Toads live mostly on land. Frogs have longer legs, while toads have shorter legs.

Complete the Compare and Contrast Worksheet for this story.

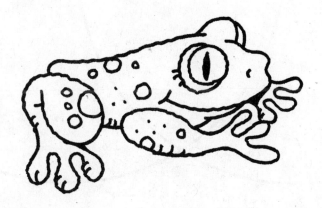

Summarizing Strategies Grade 2, SV 9781419099861

Name _____ Date _____

Compare and Contrast Worksheet

Story Title _____

Complete the Venn Diagram based on what you've read.

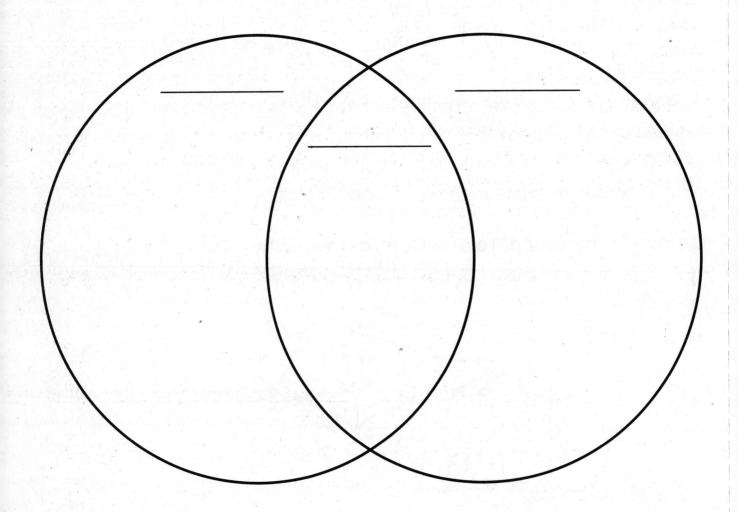

Summary: Use the information in the Venn Diagram to write a summary of the story.

_____

_____

_____

Summarizing Strategies Grade 2, SV 9781419099861

Analyzing Characters

Presentation and Model

Strategy: Analyzing characters in a story

Sometimes an author does not tell you everything about a character, so you must analyze the character. When you analyze a character, you use facts from the story to figure out how a character thinks or feels.

Read the story below.

Joel liked to explore in the woods behind his house. While his friends looked for special rocks and leaves, Joel searched for gold. When his friends sat and watched for squirrels and deer, Joel sat hoping to see a cougar or a gorilla. One day they reached a nearby cave.

"This is the empty cave I told you about," said one boy. "My dad and I have been inside. We've found lots of arrowheads." Joel quickly followed him into the cave. "Maybe I'll find some pirate treasure!" he added.

Complete the Character Profile Diagram based on what you've read.

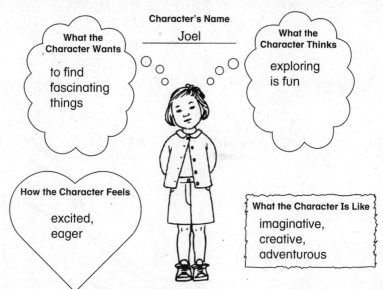

Character's Name
Joel

What the Character Wants
to find fascinating things

What the Character Thinks
exploring is fun

How the Character Feels
excited, eager

What the Character Is Like
imaginative, creative, adventurous

Summary: Use the information in the Character Profile Diagram to write a summary of the story.

Joel searches for fascinating things like gold and big animals. Joel and his friends explore the woods and find a cave. Joel is excited and eager to look for pirate treasure.

Summarizing Strategies Grade 2, SV 9781419099861

Analyzing Characters

Read the story below.

The Walk to School

Rebekah walked to school with her brother. Everything seemed to make him sad. He saw a tree branch lying on the ground. "Too bad that tree has a broken branch. It looked so nice before."

"That's okay," said Rebekah. "Now there's more room for a new branch to grow." Then her brother pointed out an old house. He thought the peeling paint was ugly. "Well, when it is painted, people will really notice how beautiful it is."

When they saw an empty flower bed, her brother said it was sad that nobody took care of it.

"I think the people are picking out the perfect flower seeds," said Rebekah. "Sometimes that takes a little bit more time." Her brother felt better.

Complete the Analyzing Characters Worksheet for this story.

Analyzing Characters
Summarizing Strategies Grade 2, SV 9781419099861

Analyzing Characters

Read the story below.

Caroline Takes the Stage

Caroline's legs shook as she walked out onto the stage. She looked out at the sea of faces. Caroline wiped the sweat from her brow. Her hands trembled as she picked up the microphone. Caroline wished that she were able to disappear. "I know I can do this," Caroline said to herself.

Caroline thought about all the times she sang this song at home. Caroline closed her eyes and tried to relax. She opened her eyes and looked out at the front row. Caroline was relieved to see her mother and father. Caroline smiled and began to sing.

Complete the Analyzing Characters Worksheet for this story.

Name _____ Date _____

Analyzing Characters Worksheet

Story Title _____

Complete the Character Profile Diagram based on what you've read.

Summary: Use the information in the Character Profile Diagram to write a summary of the story.

_____

_____

_____

Making Predictions

Presentation and Model

Strategy: Making predictions in a story

You make predictions when you use information in a story to figure out what may happen next.

Read the story below.

William and his family lived on a farm. William had a pet pig named Molly. Every morning, William got up early to feed Molly. He filled a bucket with food for her. She just loved to eat. When Molly saw William coming with her food, she ran quickly to him. "Oink! Oink!" she said.

William ran alongside Molly's pen after school. Molly ran, too. "Oink! Oink!" William often gave her a bath. She squealed in delight. "Oink! Oink!" In the evening, William brought her treats after dinner. William smiled. He knew what was coming next!

Complete the Prediction Chart based on what you've read.

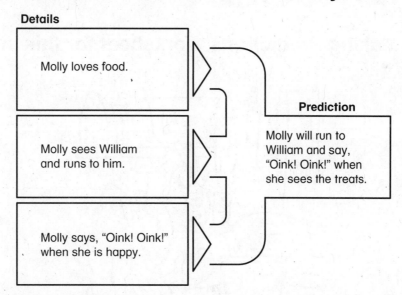

Details

Molly loves food.

Molly sees William and runs to him.

Molly says, "Oink! Oink!" when she is happy.

Prediction

Molly will run to William and say, "Oink! Oink!" when she sees the treats.

Summary: Use the information in the Prediction Chart to write a summary of the story.

Molly oinks and runs to greet William when she sees her food. She oinks and plays when he runs or gives her a bath. When he gets ready to feed her treats, she will probably oink and run to him.

Making Predictions

Read the story below.

Hen Bakes a Cake

Hen wanted to bake a cake. She got out the eggs, butter, and flour. "Oh, I almost forgot the mixing bowl," she said. "Now where did I put it?" Hen looked around. Finally she found it on a shelf. "Oh dear, I am so forgetful."

Hen turned the oven on and went about her business. She did not know that she made the oven too hot. Hen mixed everything in the bowl. Then she poured the cake batter into a pan. Hen placed the pan in the oven. She forgot to set the timer.

Hen went outside to chat with Goat and lost track of time. When she came into the house she sniffed the air. The bad smell was coming from the kitchen.

Complete the Making Predictions Worksheet for this story.

Summarizing Strategies Grade 2, SV 9781419099861

Making Predictions

Read the story below.

The Soccer Ball

Heidi ran home from school. She couldn't wait to play soccer with her friends. Glen and Laurel came over after school. "Watch this," said Glen. He kicked the ball in the air and bounced it off of his head.

"Let's see you kick like you did in last week's game," Glen said to Laurel. Laurel kicked the ball high in the air. Heidi watched as the ball zoomed past her head toward the window of her house. Uncle Barry came out of nowhere and jumped in front of the window.

Complete the Making Predictions Worksheet for this story.

Summarizing Strategies Grade 2, SV 9781419099861

Name _____ Date _____

Teacher's Toolbox

Making Predictions Worksheet

Story Title _____

Complete the Prediction Chart based on what you've read.

Details

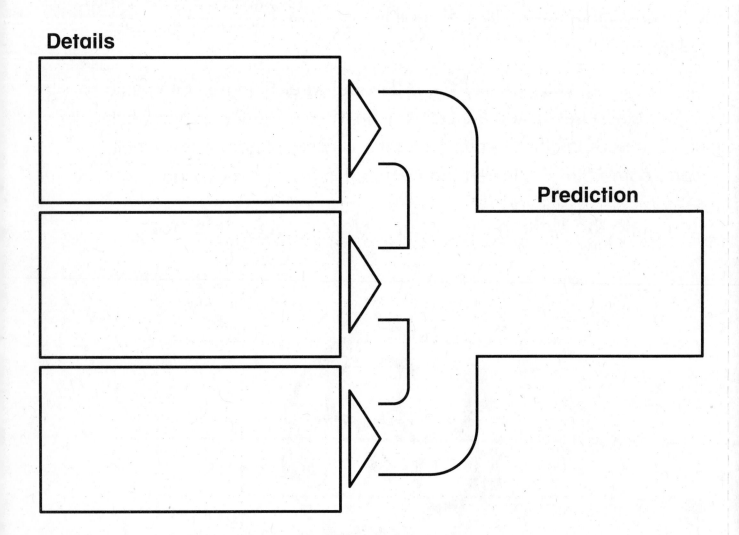

Prediction

Summary: Use the information in the Prediction Chart to write a summary of the story.

_____

_____

_____

Making Predictions
Summarizing Strategies Grade 2, SV 9781419099861

Understanding Graphics

Presentation and Model
Strategy: Reading graphics to understand a story

Graphics are charts, tables, and diagrams that give information. You can better understand a story when you study the information in the graphic.

Read the story below.

Mr. Li's class wanted to know what flavor of ice cream the class liked best. Mr. Li made a chart. "I am giving each of you a paper ice cream cone," said Mr. Li. "When I call your name, tape your cone in your favorite row." After Mr. Li had called all the names, the class studied the chart.

Favorite Kinds of Ice Cream

Strawberry	🍦🍦🍦🍦
Chocolate	🍦🍦🍦🍦🍦🍦
Vanilla	🍦🍦🍦🍦🍦
Mint	🍦🍦

Complete the Q Matrix based on what you've read.

	Strawberry	Chocolate	Vanilla	Mint
How many?	4	7	5	2
Most favorite?		✓		
Least favorite?				✓

Summary: Use the information in the Q Matrix to write a summary of the story.

Mr. Li's class wanted to know which flavor of ice cream most students liked. After each student made a choice, Mr. Li's class found out that chocolate was their favorite kind of ice cream.

Understanding Graphics

Read the story below.

The Food Drive

The food shelter in Juan's neighborhood had a canned food drive. The shelter was collecting cans of food to give to hungry people. The workers at the shelter put the cans on the shelves. Many of the shelves were still empty. Juan and his friends Dan, Kate, and Rosa wanted to help.

On Saturday they brought cans of food to the shelter. They gave them to the workers. Juan felt happy that he and his friends could help.

Complete the Understanding Graphics Worksheet for this story.

Number of Cans We Collected

Understanding Graphics

Read the story below.

Learning the States

Mr. Long wanted his students to learn about different states. Mr. Long told the class to check out library books to read at home. Carrie wanted to learn about Texas. Nick and Elena wanted to check out lots of books about Florida. Don loved Colorado. His aunt and uncle lived there.

Mr. Long made a chart. The students kept track of how many books they read. "Keep reading," said Mr. Long. "By the end of the year, you will be a state smartie!"

Complete the Understanding Graphics Worksheet for this story.

Books Read

Carrie	📖 📖
Nick	📖 📖 📖 📖 📖
Elena	📖
Don	📖 📖 📖 📖

Summarizing Strategies Grade 2, SV 9781419099861

Name _____ Date _____

Understanding Graphics Worksheet

Story Title _____

Complete the Q Matrix based on what you've read.

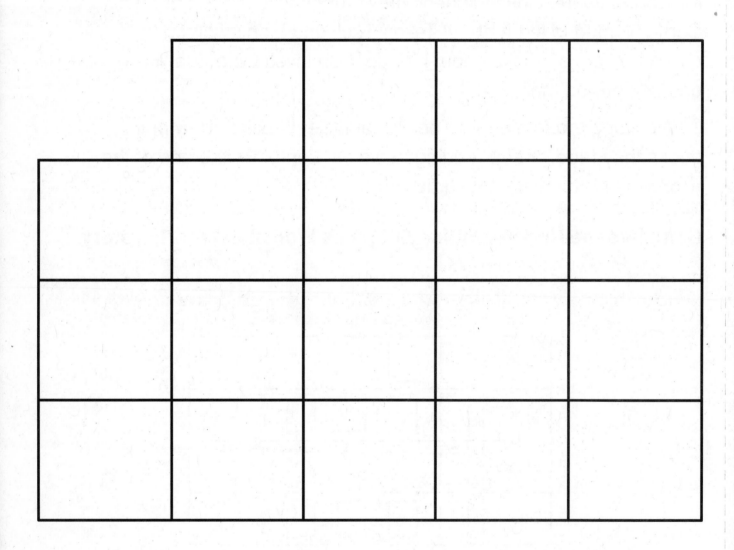

Summary: Use the information in the Q Matrix to write a summary of the story.

_____

_____

_____

Summarizing Strategies Grade 2, SV 9781419099861

Drawing Conclusions

Presentation and Model

Strategy: Drawing conclusions in a story

You can use facts from a story along with what you already know to draw a conclusion about a character or an event in a story.

Read the story below.

Sometimes it rains a lot in the mountains. When it rains a lot, the rivers can flood. When the rivers flood, the water can hurt animals, trees, and houses.

What can stop the flooding? A dam can hold back the water so it can't flood. Beavers can make very good dams. They cut down trees with their strong teeth. They put the trees across the stream from bank to bank. They fill in the spaces between the logs with mud and sticks. This stops the water. Sometimes forest rangers catch beavers and fly them to streams where dams need to be built very quickly.

Complete the Everything Points to It diagram based on what you've read.

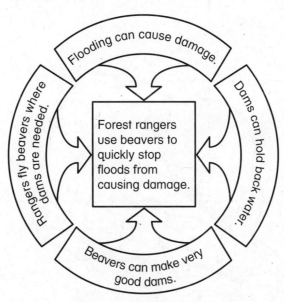

Flooding can cause damage.

Rangers fly beavers where dams are needed.

Dams can hold back water.

Forest rangers use beavers to quickly stop floods from causing damage.

Beavers can make very good dams.

Summary: Use the information in the Everything Points to It diagram to write a summary of the story.

Beavers can make very good dams. Their dams can hold back strong

flood water. Forest rangers use beavers to quickly stop floods.

Summarizing Strategies Grade 2, SV 9781419099861

Drawing Conclusions

Read the story below.

Grandpa and Ming

Grandpa and Ming packed lunch in a basket. Ming packed the cheese and carrot sticks. Grandpa made lemonade. He poured it into a bottle. They both made their favorite sandwiches. They put meat and cheese on the bread. Then they added lots of pickles.

Grandpa and Ming hopped into the truck. Grandpa drove to their favorite spot. They spread out the blanket. Ming built a castle in the sand. Grandpa collected shells. The shore was full of seagulls. Soon the sun began to set. Grandpa and Ming packed up their things. They drove home and talked about their day. Ming couldn't wait until they went back again.

Complete the Drawing Conclusions Worksheet for this story.

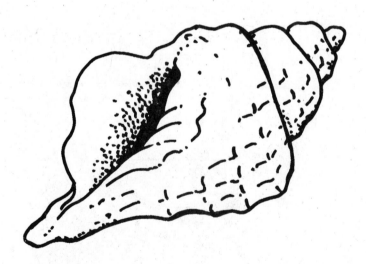

Drawing Conclusions
Summarizing Strategies Grade 2, SV 9781419099861

Drawing Conclusions

Read the story below.

Anna's Surprise

It was Anna's eighth birthday. "I have a big surprise for you, Anna," said her mom. Anna looked at the surprise. "Oh, how cute! It's what I've always wanted!" Anna squealed. She looked at her mom in delight.

"Hold out your hands," said Anna's mom. "Be careful. You have to be very gentle."

Mom slowly placed the surprise in Anna's hands. Her surprise was covered with gray and white fur. It opened its tiny mouth and said, "Meow."

Anna smiled and looked up at her mom. "I think my surprise needs a bowl of milk!" said Anna.

Anna's mom laughed. "I think you are right!" Anna and her mom went into the kitchen.

Complete the Drawing Conclusions Worksheet for this story.

Name _____ Date _____

Drawing Conclusions Worksheet

Story Title _____

Complete the Everything Points to It diagram based on what you've read.

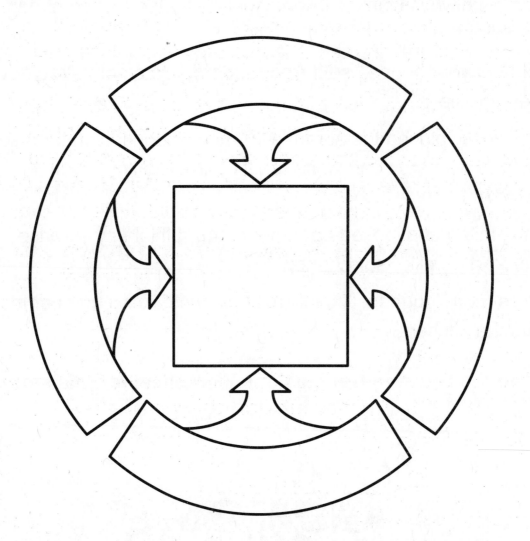

Summary: Use the information in the Everything Points to It diagram to write a summary of the story.

_____

_____

_____

Making Inferences

Presentation and Model
Strategy: Making inferences in a story

Sometimes an author does not tell you everything in a story. You must get clues from the story and make an inference, or logical guess, by figuring out what is happening or what a character is feeling.

Read the story below.

Tran and his friends were so excited. They entered the theme park. Tran and his friends looked around at all the rides. "This place is so much fun!" he exclaimed. His friends agreed.

Tran and his friends waited in a long line to buy tickets. Tran looked eagerly at The Dragon. He watched as people climbed into their seats. Then the bars came down over everyone's lap. Now everyone was safe. The Dragon climbed the tracks. Then it rolled down and looped around. At the end everyone was breathless and excited!

Complete the Follow the Clues diagram based on what you've read.

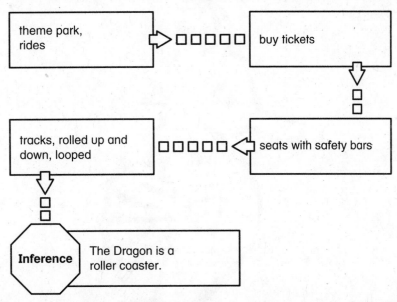

| theme park, rides | ⇨ □□□□□ | buy tickets |

| tracks, rolled up and down, looped | □□□□□ ⇦ | seats with safety bars |

Inference: The Dragon is a roller coaster.

Summary: Use the information in the Follow the Clues diagram to write a summary of the story.

Tran and his friend were excited about going to a theme park. As they waited in line for tickets, Tran watched people have fun riding The Dragon roller coaster.

Making Inferences

Read the story below.

The Seahorse

Scientists classify animals into groups so they can study them. They put animals that are alike in the same group. For example, gorillas, monkeys, and apes are part of the same group.

Scientists talked a lot about the seahorse. It has a head like a horse and a tail like a monkey, but it lives in the ocean like a fish. What group did the seahorse belong in? They could not decide. Finally, scientists agreed. Today, the seahorse is part of the fish family. Seahorses and fish have a lot in common.

Complete the Making Inferences Worksheet for this story.

Making Inferences

Read the story below.

Rabbit's Room

Rabbit went into his bedroom. What a sight! He stepped over a pile of books on the floor. Clothes were heaped on a chair. Carrots and celery covered the nightstand.

Hedgehog came over to borrow a book. "Oh my, Rabbit!" said Hedgehog. "Look at this room. How can you ever find anything?"

Rabbit looked around his room. He shrugged his shoulders. "It's simple," said Rabbit. "If I need a snack, I go to my nightstand. When I need clothes, they are in plain sight." Rabbit looked at Hedgehog thoughtfully. "You may borrow a book, Hedgehog," said Rabbit. "My library pile is in the corner!"

Complete the Making Inferences Worksheet for this story.

Name _____ Date _____

Teacher's
Toolbox

Making Inferences Worksheet

Story Title _____

Complete the Follow the Clues diagram based on what you've read.

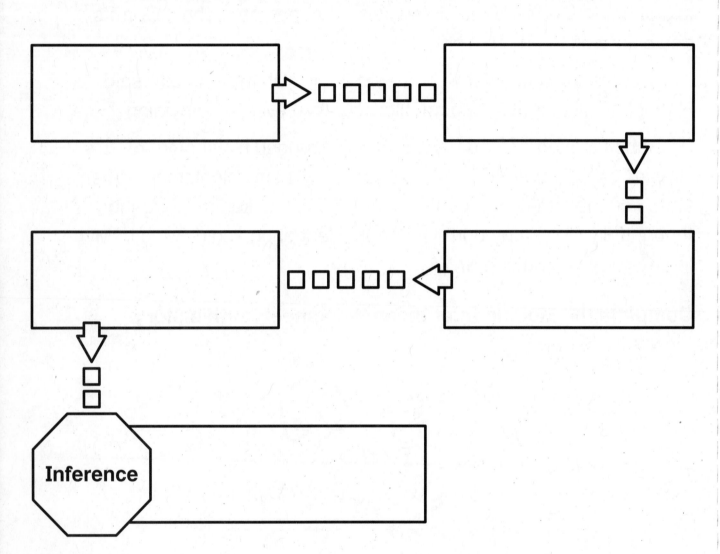

Inference

Summary: Use the information in the Follow the Clues diagram to write a summary of the story.

_____

_____

_____

Making Inferences
Summarizing Strategies Grade 2, SV 9781419099861

Author's Purpose

Presentation and Model
Strategy: Identifying the author's purpose

Authors have different reasons for writing stories. Sometimes an author wants to entertain a reader with a story. Other times an author may want to give the reader information about a subject. The reason for writing a story is called the author's purpose.

Read the story below.

Mrs. Jones loved to bake cookies. Each day the neighborhood children would come by after school. She gave each of them a cookie. No matter what kind of cookies she baked, everyone loved them.

One day Mrs. Jones was not home. A neighbor talked to the children. He said that Mrs. Jones was sick. She went to the doctor. The children had an idea. The next day they rang Mrs. Jones's doorbell. She opened the door and smiled. The children had baked dozens of cookies for Mrs. Jones.

Complete the Author's Purpose Flowchart based on what you've read.

This reading . . .			
describes a subject.	No	has characters and setting.	Mrs. Jones, children, Mrs. Jones' house after school
gives facts and details.	No	has a beginning, middle, and ending.	gives cookies, gets sick, receives cookies
mostly informs.	No	mostly entertains.	Yes

Summary: Use the information in the Author's Purpose Flowchart to write a summary of the story.

The author wrote the story to entertain the reader. Mrs. Jones bakes cookies for the children. She gets sick one day and the children bake cookies for her.

Author's Purpose
Summarizing Strategies Grade 2, SV 9781419099861

Author's Purpose

Read the story below.

Fishing Spiders

Did you know that some spiders go fishing? They don't use a fishing pole, though. These kinds of spiders are called fishing spiders. Fishing spiders are found near lakes and ponds. They float on the leaves of water plants. They wait for fish.

You may wonder how fishing spiders catch fish. A fishing spider sticks one of its legs in the water. It wiggles its leg so that a nearby fish sees it. The fish swims closer. The fish thinks that the leg is a worm. The fish swims even closer. Then the fishing spider snatches the fish from the water. Lunchtime!

Complete the Author's Purpose Worksheet for this story.

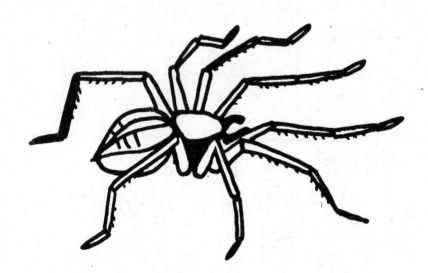

Summarizing Strategies Grade 2, SV 9781419099861

Author's Purpose

Read the story below.

Abhi's Bedroom

Abhi wanted a change. He wanted to paint his bedroom. Abhi didn't know what color to paint it. "What about blue?" asked his mother. "Then you can hang up your beach pictures and shells. Your room will remind you of the beach."

Abhi thought for a long time. "I don't think I'll paint my room after all," said Abhi. His mother looked surprised. "I know what I'd like to look at the most," he said. Abhi used clear tape and fastened his photos to the walls. "Now I can see my friends whenever I want," he said.

Complete the Author's Purpose Worksheet for this story.

Summarizing Strategies Grade 2, SV 9781419099861

Author's Purpose Worksheet

Story Title _____

Complete the Author's Purpose Flowchart based on what you've read.

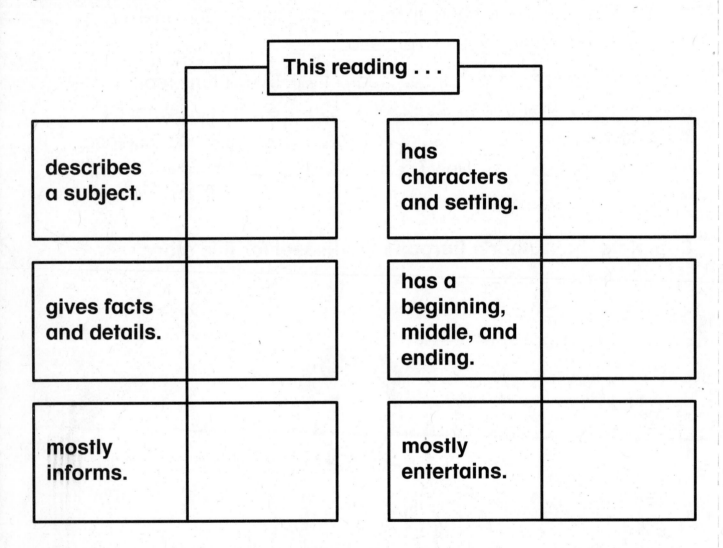

This reading . . .

describes a subject.		has characters and setting.	
gives facts and details.		has a beginning, middle, and ending.	
mostly informs.		mostly entertains.	

Summary: Use the information in the Author's Purpose Flowchart to write a summary of the story.

_____

_____

_____

Possible Answers

Page 6
Mai Paints

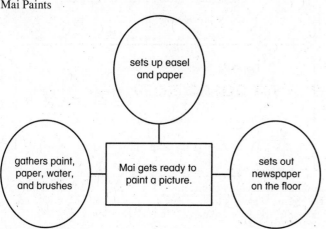

Summary: Mai gets out her art supplies so she can paint a picture.

Page 7
Justin at the Zoo

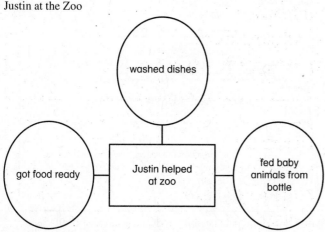

Summary: Justin helped get food ready and fed the animals at the zoo.

Page 10
Sandy Flies a Kite

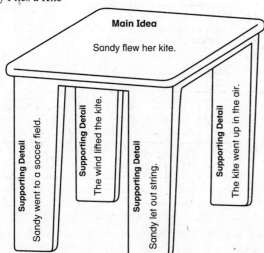

Summary: Sandy flew her kite. She went to the soccer field. The wind lifted the kite. Sandy let out more string. The kite flew up in the air.

Page 11
More Than a Game

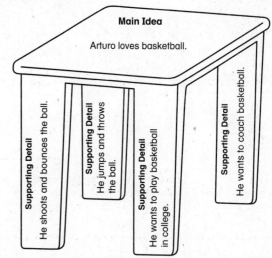

Summary: Arturo loves basketball. He jumps, shoots, and passes the ball. One day, he would like to play basketball in college and become a coach.

Page 14
Summer Fun

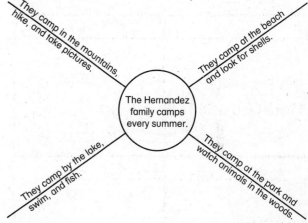

Summary: The Hernandez family likes to camp. They camp in different places and do many different things.

Summarizing Strategies Grade 2, SV 9781419099861

Page 15
The Baby Ducks

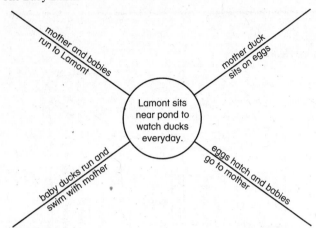

Summary: Lamont sits near a pond to watch a mother duck and her babies. Lamont watches the eggs hatch and the babies run and swim. One day the mother duck and her babies run to greet Lamont.

Page 18
Michael's Birthday Boxes

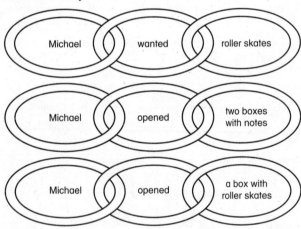

Summary: Michael wanted a pair of roller skates for his birthday. He opened two boxes with notes inside and a third box with a pair of roller skates in it.

Page 19
Jacob Starts a Story

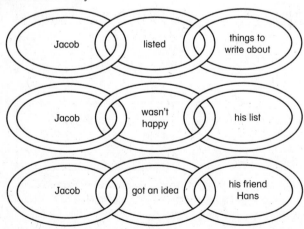

Summary: Jacob did not want to write a story about anything he wrote on his list. He saw his friend Hans and decided to write about him.

Page 22
Claudia's Big Move

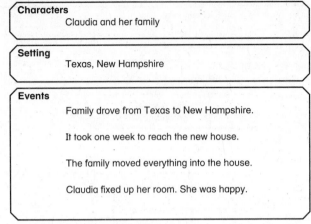

Summary: Claudia's family drove for a week from Texas to New Hampshire. They got to their new house and Claudia fixed up her room. She was happy to unpack her things and put them away.

Page 23
Amit's Aunt

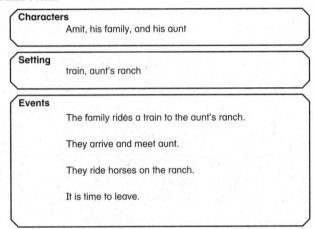

Summary: Amit and his family rode a train to visit Amit's aunt. They arrived at the train station and Amit's aunt drove them to her ranch. The family rode horses and later got ready to leave.

Page 26
Santhi and Ben at the Show

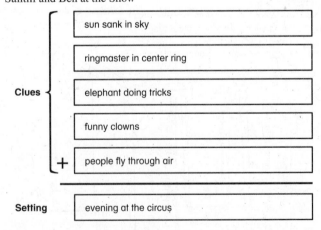

Summary: Ben and Santhi go to the circus as the sun sets in the evening. They see a ringmaster in the center ring and watch elephants do tricks and people fly through the air.

Page 27
Peter Plans Ahead

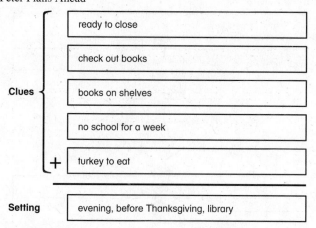

Clues
- ready to close
- check out books
- books on shelves
- no school for a week
+ turkey to eat

Setting: evening, before Thanksgiving, library

Summary: Peter goes to the library the day before the Thanksgiving holidays. The library is ready to close so he checks out lots of books to read. Peter plans to spend his week off from school reading and eating.

Page 30
Dad's Trick

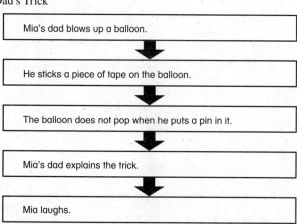

- Mia's dad blows up a balloon.
- He sticks a piece of tape on the balloon.
- The balloon does not pop when he puts a pin in it.
- Mia's dad explains the trick.
- Mia laughs.

Summary: Mia's dad blows up a balloon for a trick. He puts a piece of tape on the balloon and sticks it with a pin, but the balloon does not pop. Mia's dad explains why the balloon does not pop and Mia laughs.

Page 31
The Three Squirrels

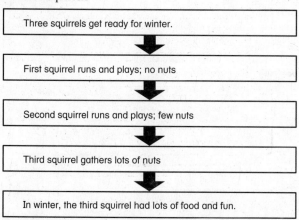

- Three squirrels get ready for winter.
- First squirrel runs and plays; no nuts
- Second squirrel runs and plays; few nuts
- Third squirrel gathers lots of nuts
- In winter, the third squirrel had lots of food and fun.

Summary: Three squirrels get ready for winter. The first squirrel runs and plays, while the second squirrel gathers a few nuts and then runs and plays. The third squirrel gathers lots of nuts and is the only one who can play in the winter.

Page 34
The Old Lot

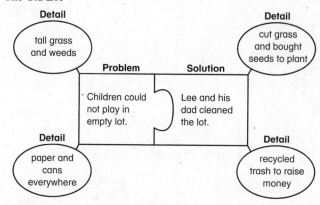

Detail: tall grass and weeds
Detail: cut grass and bought seeds to plant
Problem: Children could not play in empty lot.
Solution: Lee and his dad cleaned the lot.
Detail: paper and cans everywhere
Detail: recycled trash to raise money

Summary: Lee saw that no one took care of the empty lot across the street. It was full of trash and tall weeds, so Lee decided to clean it up. Lee's dad cut the grass and Lee planted flowers to make the lot look nice.

Page 35
Queen Hilda's Birthday

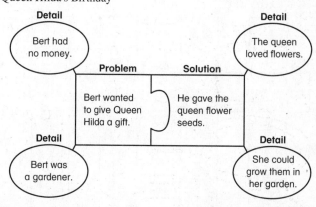

Detail: Bert had no money.
Detail: The queen loved flowers.
Problem: Bert wanted to give Queen Hilda a gift.
Solution: He gave the queen flower seeds.
Detail: Bert was a gardener.
Detail: She could grow them in her garden.

Summary: Bert had no money for Queen Hilda's gift and did not know what to do. Bert decided to give Queen Hilda flower seeds to grow in her garden.

Page 38
Volcanoes

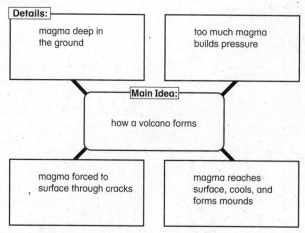

Details:
- magma deep in the ground
- too much magma builds pressure

Main Idea: how a volcano forms

- magma forced to surface through cracks
- magma reaches surface, cools, and forms mounds

Summary: A volcano forms when magma deep in the earth is forced through cracks, cools, and makes a mound.

Possible Answers
Summarizing Strategies Grade 2, SV 9781419099861

Page 39
Bats

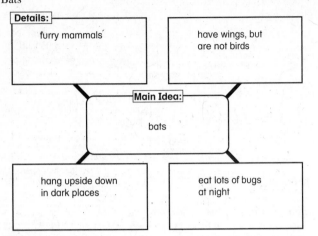

Summary: Bats are furry mammals that hang upside down in dark places and eat bugs at night.

Page 42
At the Bakery

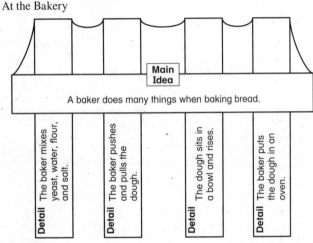

Summary: The baker does many things when baking bread. He mixes everything together and pushes and pulls the dough. The dough is left to rise and then put in an oven. The bread is baked and is then ready to be sold.

Page 43
Skyscrapers

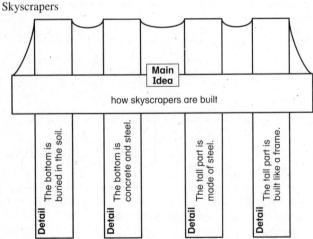

Summary: Skyscrapers are very tall buildings that are built in the city. The bottom of a skyscraper is made of concrete and steel, while the tall part is a big steel frame.

Page 46
Life of a Cactus

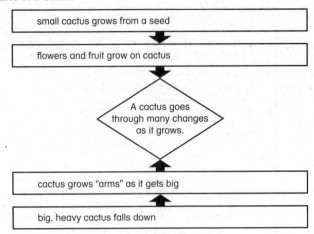

Summary: A cactus goes through many changes as it grows in a desert. The cactus starts as a seed, grows flowers and fruit, and finally becomes so heavy that it falls over.

Page 47
The Rainforest

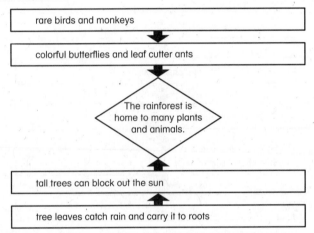

Summary: The rainforest is home to many kinds of plants and animals. There are rare animals and colorful insects. The leaves of tall trees can block the sun and catch rain that works its way down to the roots.

Possible Answers
Summarizing Strategies Grade 2, SV 9781419099861

Page 50
Pumpkins

Life Cycle of a Pumpkin

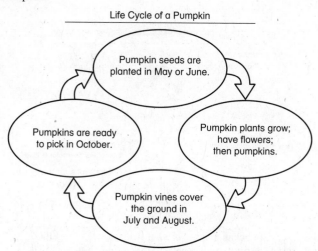

Summary: Pumpkin seeds are planted in spring and seedlings grow. The plants grow bigger, flowers bloom, and small pumpkins form. By fall the pumpkins are big enough to pick.

Page 51
Forests Return

Forests and Fires

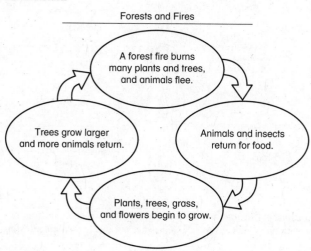

Summary: A forest goes through many changes after a fire. First, insects and small animals come back to find food. Then trees and plants begin to grow and more animals return.

Page 54
Darius and Bud

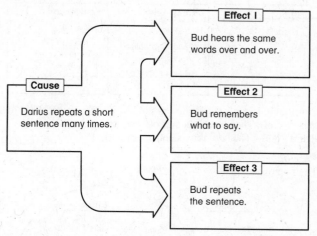

Summary: Darius loves to teach his parrot named Bud to talk. Darius repeats a short sentence so Bud gets used to hearing it. After a while, Bud remembers what to say and repeats the sentence.

Page 55
Washing the Car

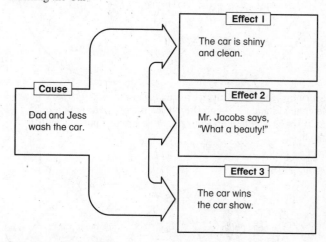

Summary: Dad and Jess decide to wash Dad's car to make it shiny and clean. Their neighbor notices how clean it is and so do the judges at the car show. Dad's car wins the car show.

Page 58
Feeding Whiskers

Word	Context Clues	Word Meaning
rammed	smack!; bowl tipped over; milk on floor	Rammed means you have hit something in a hard way.

Summary: Carly and Jill went to the kitchen to feed their cat Whiskers. Carly placed the bowl of milk on the table but Jill did not see it. Jill's elbow hit the bowl very hard and spilled the milk onto the floor.

Summarizing Strategies Grade 2, SV 9781419099861

Page 59
Lizards

Word	Context Clues	Word Meaning
shed	old skin peels off; skin underneath is new; old skin too small	Shed means old, small skin peels off and new skin is underneath.

Summary: Lizards shed their old skin, which means that the skin is peeled off. The old skin comes off when it is too small for the lizard's body. The new skin is underneath.

Page 62
The Lemonade Stand

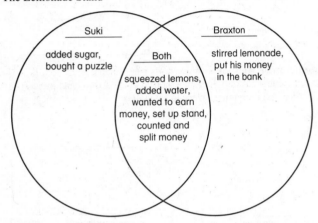

Summary: Suki and Braxton want to earn money. They set up a lemonade stand. Suki and Braxton earn money and split it in half. Suki spends her half on a puzzle, while Braxton puts his half in the bank.

Page 63
Frogs and Toads

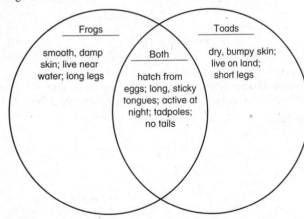

Summary: Frogs and toads are alike and different. Both hatch from eggs and become tadpoles, but their skin and legs are different.

Page 66
The Walk to School

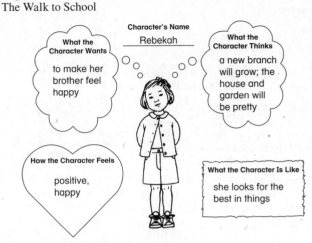

Summary: Rebekah and her brother walk to school together. Rebekah cheers him up whenever he sees something that makes him sad. Rebekah is happy and positive.

Page 67
Caroline Takes the Stage

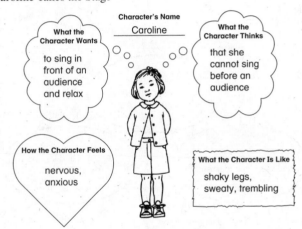

Summary: Caroline is nervous about singing on stage in front of an audience. She tries to relax, sees her parents, and is able to sing.

Page 70
Hen Bakes a Cake

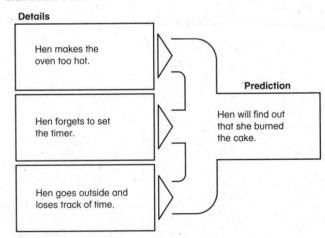

Summary: Hen wants to bake a cake but she is very forgetful. She makes the oven too hot. Hen forgets to set the timer and goes outside. When she comes back the cake has burned.

Page 71
The Soccer Ball

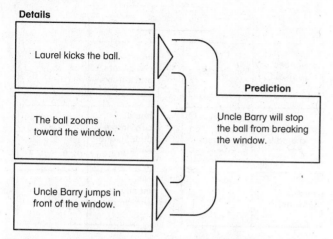

Summary: Heidi and her friends play soccer in the yard. Laurel kicks the ball high and it zooms toward a window. Uncle Barry jumps in front of the window to keep it from breaking.

Page 74
The Food Drive

	Juan	Dan	Kate	Rosa
How many?	5	4	7	6
Most cans?			✓	
Least cans?		✓		

Summary: Juan and his friends bring cans of food to the food shelter. Kate is able to bring more cans than anybody. The four friends are happy to give their cans to the workers.

Page 75
Learning the States

	Carrie	Nick	Elena	Don
How many?	2	5	1	4
Most books?		✓		
Least books?			✓	

Summary: Mr. Long told his students to check out books so they could read about states. Mr. Long make a chart to show how many books each student read. Nick read more books than anyone else.

Page 78
Grandpa and Ming

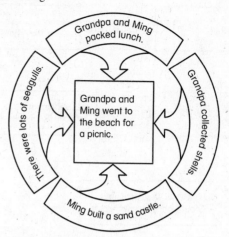

Summary: Ming and Grandpa had a picnic at the beach. They built sandcastles, collected shells, and watched seagulls. At sunset they packed up their things and drove home.

Page 79
Anna's Surprise

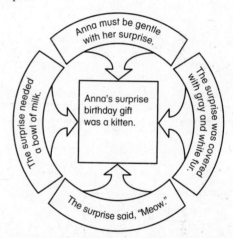

Summary: Anna's surprise birthday present was a kitten. The kitten was covered with gray and white fur. The kitten said, "Meow," and Anna said that her kitten needed a bowl of milk.

Possible Answers
Summarizing Strategies Grade 2, SV 9781419099861

Page 82
The Seahorse

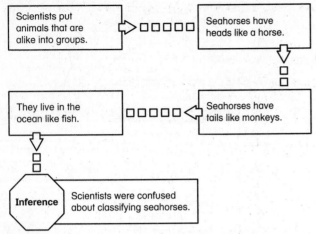

Summary: Scientists were puzzled because the seahorse seems like lots of animals. It has a head like a horse, a tail like a monkey, and swims like a fish. Finally, scientists agreed that the seahorse is most like a fish.

Page 83
Rabbit's Room

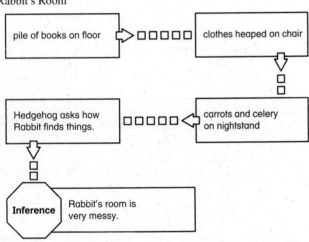

Summary: Rabbit's room is very messy. He piles things on the floor and a chair. He leaves food beside his bed. Hedgehog comes over to borrow a book and notices the mess.

Page 86
Fishing Spiders

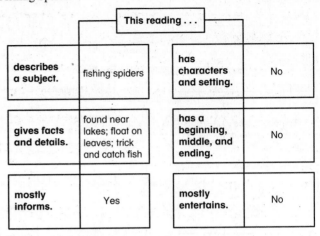

Summary: Fishing spiders live near lakes and float on leaves of water plants. Fishing spiders wait to catch fish when they swim by. This story gives facts and details about spiders.

Page 87
Abhi's Bedroom

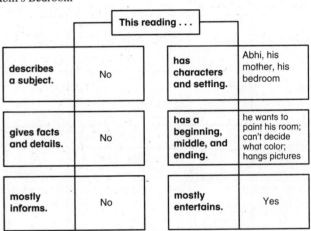

Summary: Abhi wants to paint his bedroom but can't decide what color. His mom tries to help him choose, but he decides to hang photos on the wall instead. This story entertains the reader.